D0923420

TWAYNE'S WORLD AUTHOR'S SERIES

A Survey of the World's Literature

Sylvia E. Bowman, Indiana University

GENERAL EDITOR

GREECE

Mary P. Gianos, Detroit Institute of Technology

EDITOR

Hippocrates

(TWAS 165)

TWAYNE'S WORLD AUTHORS SERIES (TWAS)

The purpose of TWAS is to survey the major writers —novelists, dramatists, historians, poets, philosophers, and critics—of the nations of the world. Among the national literatures covered are those of Australia, Canada, China, Eastern Europe, France, Germany, Greece, India, Italy, Japan, Latin America, New Zealand, Poland, Russia, Scandinavia, Spain, and the African nations, as well as Hebrew, Yiddish, and Latin Classical literatures. This survey is complemented by Twayne's United States Authors Series and English Authors Series.

The intent of each volume in these series is to present a critical-analytical study of the works of the writer; to include biographical and historical material that may be necessary for understanding, appreciation, and critical appraisal of the writer; and to present all material in clear, concise English—but not to vitiate the scholarly content of the work by doing so.

HIPPOCRATES

By EDWIN BURTON LEVINE

University of Illinois

Twayne Publishers, Inc.   ::   New York

for

MYRA
WILLIAM
and
PATRICIA

medico diligenti, priusquam conetur aegro adhibere medicinam, non solum morbus eius, cui mederi volet, sed etiam consuetudo valentis et natura corporis cognoscenda est.
Cicero, *De oratore*, 2. 44. 186

(Before he tries to apply his skills to the patient, the careful doctor must not only know the illness which he wants to heal but also the habit of the man in health and the nature of the body.)

". . . modern medicine is but a series of commentaries and elaborations on the Hippocratic writings. . . ."

—"Hippocrates in Modern Dress," Chapter XII of *Man Adapting,* The Silliman Foundation Lectures (1965), p. 323, by René Dubos.

Preface

ONE of the most interesting contributions of Greek thought of the fifth and fourth centuries B.C. was the development of an extensive medical literature. This literature is remarkable in itself and also for its subsequent influence. There has been a growing body of commentary and research into the ancient medical literature as a result of increased awareness of its complexity and importance. The inception of the modern period of interest may be dated with the publication in 1839 of the first volume of the *Oeuvres complètes d'Hippocrate,* with the copious commentary and annotations of the translator, Emile Littré, and completed in 1861 with the publication of the tenth and final volume in the set.

Less well known than Greek philosophy, and much less understood, ancient Greek medical thought has important ties to philosophy which are receiving more attention than ever before. But the greatest achievement of early medicine was to differentiate itself from both philosophy and religion. It thereby became a profession with a substance and dignity coequal to those of other *technai* or professions. It is, in fact, the only profession for which we still retain to a significant extent the written record of its genesis. In a time of increasing professionalism, this genesis of the medical profession is exciting and highly instructive. We need to know and understand a great deal more about this development if we are to understand more deeply the evolution of medical practice in our own times. We have also in the Greek instance a paradigm of the genesis of any profession.

The writings in the Hippocratic Collection are characterized by great diversity of subject, length, and style, as well as of comparative value. Here we have highly technical essays, exposition, research notes, instructional literature, advice, exhortation, polemic, philosophic excursus, case histories (the earliest recorded), *materia medica,* all sorts of lists of diseases, cures, and therapies, theoretical speculation, pragmatics of practice, dietetics (including whole inventories of good and bad comestibles and potables, with explanations of what makes each good or bad, as the case may be), the rationale for medical intervention in various illnesses, a medical concept of health, a clinical and theoretical examination of disease in general as well as of particular diseases, discussions of category and classification, and a whole set of examinations of professional behavior. To all these we must add works of both meteorological and anthropological nature in which we can clearly see the beginnings of both applied and theoretical climatology and ethnology, also the first statement of environmental medicine, and perhaps the first ethology. Small wonder then that the Collection continues to exercise its fascination!

Somehow, in ways not yet unraveled, a substantial portion of the Greek medical literature of the classical period became associated into a library of writings called the Hippocratic Collection, in honor of the most prestigious physician of the era in which the practice of medicine became rational and purified from superstition. The Collection as it has come down to us cannot now be ascribed in its various parts to particular authors. Much as we should like to do this, the evidence for individual authorship of this or that essay in the Collection simply does not exist, though there does exist at least the possibility that some lucky discovery will some day rescue from oblivion the authorship of one or more of the writings in the Collection.

It is beyond the space at my disposal in this book to examine more than a portion of the writings in the Collection. A whole chapter on anatomy has in fact been sacrificed to make room for the rest. I have tried, therefore, to include those essays which seemed to me to have the greatest claim on my attention at this time, including some of those with the widest reputation, as well as others, less regarded, which appeared germane to the framework of my discussion.

Two sorts of investigators have applied themselves to the Hippocratic Collection, almost all of whom retained their enthusiasm and respect for the total achievement of the Collection. Many physicians have studied in the Collection, not surprisingly, and with results as varied as their scholarship. But most of the students of the Collection have been philologists. I need not therefore apologize for being one of the latter group, although, like others in this group, I am made recurrently aware of my own medical ignorance. Interpretation of most materials is subject to doubt or controversy, especially with texts as ancient as these. I have for the most part indicated the doubt and eschewed the controversy, as seemed appropriate for a work of this kind. Both the doubt and the controversy can be pursued further by those interested if they will refer to the Selected Bibliography appended to this discussion.

Above all, I should like to record my gratitude to my wife for the encouragement she has given to my efforts and which has offset successive moments of diffidence on my part.

I am indebted to Professor Mary P. Gianos, of the Detroit Institute of Technology, the editor of this series, for several most helpful suggestions, from which this book has benefited; I am obliged to Mr. Frank Kirk, Editor of Twayne Publishers, Inc., for rescuing me from many a lapse of pen or typewriter. Needless to say, any errors of omission, inclusion, or interpretation remain mine.

Contents

Chronology

(No chronology has yet been established for the essays contained in the Hippocratic Collection. There is, however, general agreement among students of the Collection that the earliest essays may belong to the fifth century B.C., and the latest no more than two centuries thereafter. What follows, therefore, is a chronology intended solely to place the Collection as a whole within a developing context of events and ideas in the Aegean ring of lands and waters of the first millennium before Christ.)*

1184 Siege and fall of Troy. (Traditional date.)
1200– Amalgamation of Aeolic, Ionic, and Doric invaders
900 of the Helladic Aegean. Decay of Minoan culture.
850 Homeric epics, *Iliad* and *Odyssey,* composed.
750– Alcman, Callinus, Sappho, Alcaeus, Archilochus,
650 and Hesiod the outstanding earliest post-Homeric
poets. Early colonization of the Mediterranean.
585 (May 28) Solar eclipse predicted by Thales of Miletus.
600– Pre-Socratic philosophers: the Milesians, Thales,
500 Anaximander, and Anaximenes; Pythagoras, Alcmaeon, Xenophanes, Heraclitus. The transition from *tyranny* to *polity* in geographically separate regions of Greater Hellas. The predominance of Persia.
490– Defeat of Persia. Classic period of ancient Greece.
390 Aeschylus, Pindar, Sophocles, Aristophanes, Euripides. Hegemony and catastrophe of Athens. Age of sophistry. Flowering of Hellenic culture. Age of Pericles. Athens the

---

* The chronology is traditional and speculative, or borrowed chiefly from the *Greek-English Lexicon* compiled originally by Henry George Liddell and Robert Scott, new (ninth) edition completed 1940 and reprinted with a Supplement in 1968, and *A History of Greek Philosophy* by W. K. C. Guthrie, volumes 1-3 (all published to date), 1962-1969.

school of Greece. Miltiades and Themistocles. Pre-Socratic philosophers: the Eleatics and Ionians, Parmenides, Zeno, Melissus, Empedocles, Anaxagoras. Leucippus and Democritus. Protagoras, Gorgias, Prodicus, Thrasymachus, Alcidamas, Lycophron, and other sophists. Socrates. Pheidias and the embellishment of the Acropolis.

CHAPTER 1

The Mystery of Hippocrates and the Hippocratic Collection

NO sooner has one read the very first sentence of the *Life of Hippocrates* attributed to Soranus, than he realizes that the myths after Hippocrates early filled that vacuum which popular history abhors. The truth was simply ignored in favor of all sorts of nonsense calculated to dazzle the innocent and impress the gullible. Where we should be pleased, much more than merely content, to have the facts of his ancestry, birth (including the all-important dates of birth and death), and a scheme at least of his youthful training and subsequent professional activity through the years of his maturity, the surviving biographical notes tell us only the wonderful, the miraculous, the improbable, or the impossible.

I *Hippocrates*: *Man, Hero, Myth*: *The Legendary Treatment of the Beginnings of Medical Science*

The *Life* according to Soranus begins by saying that Hippocrates was a native of Cos, the son of Herakleidas and Phainaretê, and traces his ancestry to the twentieth and nineteenth generations, respectively, as far back as Heracles and Asklepios. This absurd genealogy is said to be attested by Eratosthenes, Pherekydes, Apollodorus, and Areios of Tarsos. He became the pupil first of his father, Herakleidas, then of Herodikos, but according to some sources he was (somehow) also the pupil of Gorgias of Leontini, the Sicilian rhetorician, as well as of the philosopher Democritus of Abdera (in Thrace).

He reached his peak of activity during the period of the Peloponnesian War (presumably the last quarter of the fifth century is meant, for the war spanned the years 431–404 B.C.). According to Histomachos, in Book I of *The School of Hippocrates* (*Peri tes Hippokratous haireseos*), Hippocrates was born in the first year of the eightieth Olympiad, but according to Soranos of Cos who searched the archives on the island of Cos, there is an additional statement to the effect that his birth occurred during the sole archonship (characteristic of if not peculiar to, Cos) of Abriadas, on the twenty-seventh day of the month Agrianos. Soranos of Cos is also the source of the statement that to his own day the Coans continued to offer sacrifice to Hippocrates. Soranos of Cos is to be distinguished from Soranos (or Soranus) of Ephesus, the eminent physician and medical writer of the second century A.D., whose writings on midwifery, gynecology, pediatrics, and surgery, especially orthopedic surgery, have in part at least survived, and to whom the *Life of Hippocrates* here discussed was spuriously ascribed long ago.[1]

After completing his medical training and general education *tois enkykliois mathemasi*)—it is interesting to note the inclusion so specifically of the latter in view of the recent return to an emphasis on general studies or liberal arts or the humanities, if you will, in the training of medical students in the last half of our own century—upon the death of his parents, Hippocrates left his native country. A malicious remark ascribed to Andreas' iatric genealogy gives as the reason for Hippocrates' departure from Cos the burning of the archives on the neighboring isthmus of Cnidos, where a rival school of medicine flourished. The arsonist allegedly was Hippocrates!

Others, more generous, explain Hippocrates' departure from Cos as based on the conscious intent to observe what had been achieved in other places and to thus diversify his own experience. Soranos of Cos, however, records as a fact that Hippocrates had a dream or vision which told him to settle in the land of the Thessalians. Since the ancient Greeks took dreams both seriously and portentously, the remark is culturally plausible, even if without factual substance.

He was so much admired for his service to all of Greece that he was urged by King Perdiccas of Macedonia, who was thought to be consumptive, to come to him with Euryphon, his senior, at public expense, and to determine for himself whether his sickness was a mortal one. It seems that after the death of his father Alexandros he had fallen in love with Phila, the latter's concubine. The curious passage which follows seems to mean that Hippocrates explained what had happened to the king, watched closely the development of the disease, and the king's complete alteration, and succeeded in arresting the disease. The king recovered.

Hippocrates was invited by the Abderites to visit them and heal the philosopher Democritus of his madness, as well as to rid the whole city of the plague. There does not seem to be any reason to believe this story either.

When the plague attacked the country of Illyria and also Paeonia in Macedonia, and the rulers of these countries invited Hippocrates to come to them, he asked their ambassadors about the prevailing winds in their countries, and then dismissed them, without their achieving the purpose of their mission. He had calculated that the disease would descend upon Attica, and after predicting what would happen, he turned his attention to the welfare of the cities of Greece and to his students.

He was such a staunch patriot that his fame reached even the Persians. This led to an invitation from Artaxerxes, through Hystanis the satrap of the province of the Hellespont, supported by handsome gifts. Hippocrates refused the offer. His refusal was attributed by the biographer (or fantasist) to his sense of honor, his indifference to money, and his love for his family. An extant letter is cited as evidence for the offer and its refusal.

What other marvelous things did this busy physician achieve? For one, he rescued his native land when it was threatened with war by the Athenians by asking aid of the Thessalians. Hence his dazzling honors from the people of Cos, but he also won them from the Thessalians, the Argives, and the Athenians. The latter, by public consent, even initiated him into the Eleusinian mysteries, a distinction he shared only with Heracles. They also conferred Athenian citizenship upon him and granted to his descendants the right to meals in the prytaneum (city hall), gratis of course.

He taught his profession to his kinsmen ungrudgingly, after administering to them the appropriate Oath (or perhaps, in compliance with the terms of it).

He died at Larissa (in Thessaly) in the same year as Democritus is said to have died. Some give his age at death as eighty, others as eighty-five, still others as one hundred and four and even one hundred and nine! He was buried midway between the two towns of Larissa and Gyrton. His tomb was still pointed out in the time of his biographer. For a long time, a swarm of bees produced honey in the tomb, which wet nurses in the vicinity successfully used as a salve to cure their babies of thrush.

The *Bios* ("Biography") preserves for us what is probably a historically truthful tradition concerning the appearance and features of Hippocrates: "he is depicted in the many likenesses of him with his head covered as some say with a felt cap, indicating his noble birth, like Odysseus; but others (say) it is a *himation* (*i.e.,* cloth), and some of them ascribe its use to the wearer's sense of dignity, since he was bald (on top?), while others attribute it to the sensitivity of his scalp (*dia to asthenes tes kephales,* literally 'weakness of his head'), and still others say it was by way of suggesting the necessity of protecting the vital spot of the body. But there were yet other interpretations of this mysterious headcovering: to some it was a symbol of the man's fondness for travel, to others a symbol of the lack of clarity in his writings, for others it represented the necessity to protect oneself against harm even when well, and finally, some thought it indicated the physician's concern to keep his hands free of interference by keeping the loose ends of his outer garment (the himation) gathered together over his head." It was this very description which led to the discovery of the genuine likeness of Hippocrates at Ostia by the archaeologist Giovanni Becatti, as reported by him in an article published in 1946.[2]

The question of the authenticity of his writings was debated in antiquity, and there was little agreement. The many conflicting judgments about his writings or those attributed to him only made decision difficult: first, regarding the titles of his works; second, the ability to observe the distinctive character of his style; third, the fact that he wrote in one and the same style when in his full vigor, but elsewhere because of age revealed greater weakness. Still other reasons were conceivable to explain difficulties of interpretation of the writings.

On his death he left two sons, Thessalos and Dracon, and a large number of students, but his own sons are said to have been the most brilliant of them all.

The tenth-century lexicon called the Suidas repeats some of the above in condensed fashion but often in identical words. We learn from it that Hippocrates' works were revered as the "words of a god, not the utterances of a mere mortal." The first book, according to this account, contained the Oath, the second the Prognoses, and the third the Aphorisms, which is characterized as "exceeding the comprehension of men." Arranged in fourth place was the sixty-volume bulk of his work, well known and greatly admired, which "comprises all medical knowledge and wisdom."

Plato, whose life (c. 429–347 B.C.) overlaps that of Hippocrates, refers to Hippocrates the Asclepiad, as the very type of the teacher of medicine, but also significantly in the same passage of the *Phaedrus* (270b–270e) he associates his name with *ho alethes logos,* "the true reason." It may be crucial for the history of philosophy and for the evolution of the socratic method if, as claimed by Louis Bourgey and others, the inspiration for the latter came from Hippocrates.[3] Again, in the *Protagoras* of Plato (311b–c), Hippocrates of Cos, the Asclepiad, is the master of his art, as Polycleitus of Argos and Pheidias of Athens were the acknowledged masters of theirs, all three teaching their art for a tuition fee.

The current influence of Hippocrates is vouched for by allusions found in the surviving works of Aristotle; the physician resident in Athens and contemporary of Aristotle, Diocles of Carystus; and Ctesias of Cnidus, who was both physician and member of the court of Artaxerxes, for whom he performed at least one mission of diplomacy, and the author of a history of Persia called *Persika,* written like the *Corpus Hippocraticum* in Ionic Greek.

That Hippocrates is a historical figure is uncontested. The argument is only concerning what he wrote.

II   *The Hippocratic Collection*

The number of works assembled in the *Corpus Hippocraticum* is impressive. In the various lists compiled in antiquity by Bacchius, Celsus, and Erotian there are seventy titles of which several are works in multivolumes. The lists of the three compilers mentioned are most conveniently compared in W. H. S. Jones's *General Introduction* (pp. xxxviii–xxxix). Erotian's list is the fullest, forty-nine titles in all, compared to twenty-three (possibly) for Bacchius and twenty-five for Celsus.

Gossen's original article for Pauly-Wissowa's *Realencyclopadie* cited a total of one hundred and fifty-eight titles, over half of which were always taken to be apocryphal and many still unprinted. Twelve more titles of works cited, but completely unknown otherwise, are listed by Gossen in the Supplementband III, col. 1154, for a total therefore of one hundred and seventy titles. Whether genuinely Hippocratic or not, the existence of so many works surviving whole, in part, or by title only , is very solid evidence of medical literary industry for the fifth and fourth centuries B.C. and possibly for the third as well.

The research of the past one hundred and fifty years has failed to determine in any acceptable degree the answers to those questions which relate to the provenance of this complex Collection. Emile Littré's notion, as proposed in his Introduction (pp. 287f.), that the Collection was brought together by order perhaps of Ptolemy II Philadelphus for the library at Alexandria which he founded, was rejected in this century by Ludwig Edelstein who agreed with Jones.[4]

Jones's summary description of the corpus needs no important modification though it was made more than forty-five years ago: "The Hippocratic collection is a medley, with no inner bond of union except that all the works are written in the Ionic dialect and are connected more or less closely with medicine or one of its allied sciences. There are the widest possible divergences of style, and the sharpest possible contradictions in doctrine."[5]

Littré's attempt at an elevenfold classification of the Collection has proved to be one of the most notable failures in what remains the most impressive and ambitious of all scholarly researches on the subject of ancient Greek medicine. Half or fewer of the twelve works which Littré admitted into his first class of genuine works of Hippocrates would be accepted today by a majority of the students of the Collection since Littré. It may be useful, however, to reproduce here Littré's list of works which he considered genuinely the product of Hippocrates:[6] *Ancient Medicine; Prognostic; Aphorisms; Epidemics, Book I and III; Regime in Acute Illnesses; Airs, Waters, Places; Articulations; Fractures; Instruments of Reduction (Mochlicon); Head Injuries; Oath;* and *Law (Medical Education)*.

For Ludwig Edelstein, who, like Littré, devoted much of his lifetime to study of the Collection, not one of the items in the above list, let alone any of those in the remaining ten classes drawn up by Littré, is genuine. His early conclusion was never subsequently abandoned that "the Hippocratic Writings have nothing in common with Hippocrates" and that "not once are there found in them doctrines which the historical Hippocrates represented."[7] It is fair to say that this complete degree of skepticism is shared by few scholars, in spite of the impressive nature of his study of the documents.

As might be expected, the scholarly literature devoted to the examination of the Collection is very extensive. The works listed in the Selected Bibliography at the end of this volume constitute only a fraction of the total output to date in the most accessible languages. Of some seventy works in the Collection itself, as it is usually constituted, I have chosen twenty as those most relevant to the discussion in this book. The tabulation which follows this introduction indicates by title those included or excluded from my discussion. In particular, all the orthopedic works have been excluded.

A List of the Hippocratic Collection

(Works discussed in the present volume are marked *)

English Title	Greek Title
Ancient Medicine*	Peri archaies ietrikes
Airs, Waters, Places*	Peri aeron hydaton topon
Prognostic	Prognostikon
Regimen in Acute Diseases*	Peri diaites oxeon
Epidemics, I and III*	Epidemiai I, III
Head Injuries	Peri ton en kephale traumaton
The Clinic*	Kat' ietreion
Fractures	Peri agmon
Joints	Peri arthron
Instruments of Reduction	Mochlikon
Aphorisms*	Aphorismoi
The Oath*	Horkos
Medical Education*	Nomos
Epidemics, II, IV-VII	Epidemiai II, IV-VII
Body Fluids*	Peri chymon
Prorrhetic, I-II	Prorrhetikon I-II
Coan Prognoses	Koakai prognoseis
The Art of Medicine*	Peri technes
The Nature of Man*	Peri physios anthropou
Regimen in Health	Peri diaites hygieines
Airs*	Peri physon
Use of Fluids	Peri chresios hygron
Diseases, I*-II*-III*	Peri nouson I-II-III
Illnesses*	Peri pathon
Human Anatomy	Peri topon ton kat' anthropon
Epilepsy, The "Sacred Disease" *	Peri hieres nousou
Ulcers	Peri helkon
Haemorrhoids	Peri haimorrhoidon
Fistulas	Peri syringon

Regimen, I*-II*-III	Peri diaites I-II-III
Dreams*	Peri enhypnion
Internal Medicine*	Peri ton entos pathon
Female Nature	Peri gynaikeies physios
Seven Months Foetus	Peri heptamenou
Eight Months Foetus	Peri oktamenou
Sperm	Peri gones
Infant Nature	Peri physios paidos
Diseases, IV	Peri nouson IV
Gynecology, I-II	Peri gynaikeion I-II
Female Sterility	Peri aphoron
Illnesses in Young Females	Peri parthenion
Superfetation	Peri epikyesios
Excision of the Foetus	Peri enkatatomes embryou
Anatomy	Peri anatomes
Dentition	Peri odontophuies
Adenography*	Peri adenon
General Physiology*	Peri sarkon
Hebdomads	Peri hebdomadon
The Heart*	Peri kardies
Nutrition and Digestion	Peri trophes
Vision	Peri opsios
Angiology*	Peri osteon physios
The Physician*	Peri ietrou
Professional Conduct*	Peri euschemosynes
Precepts*	Parangeliai
Crises	Peri krision
Critical Days	Peri krisimon
Letters	Epistolai
The Emissary Speech	Presbeutikos
Speech at the Altar of Athena	Epibomios

(Based on Littré and Jones)

CHAPTER 2

Medical Theory and Philosophy

A LL the writings in the Hippocratic Collection may be said to
have a theoretical point of view or philosophy of medicine,
yet only a small number directly examine or lay down in any
extensive way the tenets of their authors. Still, none of these
discussions is solely philosophical or theoretical. The normal habit
of each writer is to introduce particulars illustrative of the care
and treatment of the sick. These particulars often appear to be and
are intended as arguments for the validity of the generalizations
made about medicine, its rationale, its function, and its relation
to the scheme of human things.

I have grouped together in this chapter those few writings which
appear to me to best represent in somewhat discursive form their
authors' views on medicine in general. This is not quite the case
with the essay, *Body Fluids*, however, which lacks organized theoretical discussion. The play of theoretic understanding illuminates for
us a point of view, a comprehensive or embracing notion in a
philosophic framework in many of the other writings in the collection,
if not in fact in all of them.

Although somewhat arbitrary, the advantage of the arrangement
adopted here is that it serves as an introduction to the Hippocratic
writings in terms sufficiently broad to put the reader in touch with
the ideational context from which arose all the writings which will
be discussed subsequently. The remaining essays may then be
considered in terms of their particular subject and in turn related
to the generalizing statements with which this chapter is concerned.

Since the chronology of the works to be discussed is far from
certain, we are free to bring them into the discussion in any de-
sirable relationship or sequence, and for the most part no claim
is made for the anteriority of one work or concept to another.
That the ideas contained in these essays were in flux rather than
static, fixed and frozen once and for all times, is altogether probable.

Each section in this chapter is devoted to one of the six following essays: *Ancient Medicine, Airs, The Art of Medicine, Regimen I, The Nature of Man,* and *Body Fluids.*

I *Ancient Medicine*

It is attractive for many reasons to begin our consideration of Greek medical theory and philosophy by examining the essay which has the title *Ancient Medicine (Peri archaies ietrikes).* It is both a clearly stated break with the past—the centuries in which medicine labored confusedly, without fixed reference points of its own, enmeshed in the coils of philosophical speculation—and an avowal of the writer's determination to conserve what he considered valuable from the past.

Once freed from the unnecessary or irrelevant hypostatizing of philosophical speculation, medicine can be established, according to the author, on a firm and independent footing with a rationale, a method, and objectives of its own. It is then prepared to become a "science," that is to say, a branch of knowledge, although its essential and lasting connection with "art" and "technique" and "skill" is never lost sight of. Always medicine is spoken of as a *techne.* This word embraces all three of these notions, as well as those of "craft," "occupation," and "profession."

Unexpectedly, the chief illustrative material of the argument is drawn from dietetics, and to a much smaller extent from other topics, namely those of body temperature; body fluids; powers (called *dynameis*), defined as the extreme properties and forces of the humors; and figures (called *schemata*), defined as the conformation of organs within the body and on its surface.

The reason for the apparent imbalance in argumentative sources appears to be twofold. One is the conviction that dietary regulation is of supervalent importance in both healthy and morbid states. The second is a mistrust of other forms of therapy. The latter is very reasonably based on an awareness of the complexity, uncertainty, or life-threatening nature of forms of therapy other than dietary regulation. The high position of dietotherapy is repeatedly attested everywhere in the Hippocratic Collection, whereas the mistrust of other therapeutic means may or may not be explicitly stated, yet is readily inferable.

The essay begins with a criticism of those who have tried to base their investigation of the subject of medicine on narrow or oversimplified hypotheses. As examples of such hypotheses, the writer mentions the notions of the contrasts between heat and cold, wetness and dryness. This reduction of the etiology of disease and death to one or two primary and unchanging causes is in his opinion obviously wrong. The proof of his dissent from their position is based on the distinction he makes between good and bad practitioners of the art. By "good" and "bad" we are to understand "successful" as opposed to "unsuccessful."

If it were only a matter of hypothesis, the need for inquiry and discovery would be removed. Then all practitioners of medicine would be on the same level of ignorance. Chance alone would determine in such a situation the care and management of the sick. Actually, medicine, like any other art, has its good and bad practitioners. They differ from each other considerably in their handiwork and in their knowledge.

The truth of the matter is, the author of *Ancient Medicine* says, that medicine rests firmly on observation. Unlike the investigation of that time into celestial or subterranean phenomena, medicine needs no unsupported hypothesis which, from its nature, cannot be verified independently by the senses.

The importance of these two statements taken together cannot be overemphasized. It directly places medicine upon one of the two indispensable supporting pillars of science generally: the direct observation of sensorily verifiable evidence. The other supporting pillar of science, experimentation, is certainly attested or implied in most of the writings, but ancient experimentation in general lacks the organization, drive, and sophistication which typify it among the moderns. Inquiry and discovery (reading *eskepto* and *heureto* in Jones's edition) together make medicine an experimental art or science susceptible to rational modes of application.

The author claims that medicine had long possessed all the means required and that it had discovered a principle and a method to which are due many excellent discoveries over the long course of time. The remainder of what needs discovery will be discovered, he says, if capable persons, familiar with existing discoveries, base their research on the unknown upon what is already known. His term for "principle" is *arche*. For "method" he uses the term *hodos*. The method is surely that of observation and experimentation based on knowledge of previous discoveries.

It is harder to say what the author meant by "principle." This results from several complexities in his discussion. The substance of medicine is knowledge common to all mankind in their experience of states of well-being and sickness. To this must be added the knowledge of causes and cures which it is the particular duty of the practitioner to acquire. But we are closer to the "principle" on which medicine is based when the author begins his discussion of the *need* for medicine.

Men sought and invented medicine because they perceived that the regime of health could not suffice for the sick. Most of the rest of the essay is devoted to an examination of the origins of dietary treatment in which the author sees the very origins of medicine itself, with a discussion of the nature of variety in diet generally and remarks on their effects.

His notion that medicine originated in the need for dietotherapy in the varying states of sickness and health, rather than the need, for example, to deal with physical traumata or psychological conditions, is both intellectually interesting and central to his discussion. The author thought of diet as adaptive and environmentally determined.

The foods of men and animals would not be differentiated today if those of animals had sufficed to maintain human health. Only the hardiest of men could survive such a diet. Those of feebler constitution were bound to perish and did. To the present time, he says, the ability of men to adapt to a coarse diet varies with the soundness and degree of habituation of the individual. So modern diets are based on the results of this search for adequate and sensible foods in keeping with man's nature. So too, there are varieties in the preparation of foods, in an effort to make them more readily digestible and to prevent their being injurious to health.

Furthermore, these searches and inventions truly deserve the name of medicine, since upon them are based the health, the nourishment, and the safety of mankind. Wherever medicine is practiced, it has aimed at restricting and modifying the diet of those who become unwell for their bodily improvement. Thus solids have been reduced and liquids administered in increased quantities, and, by cooking in a variety of ways, the difficulties of digestion are reduced or overcome for the infirm. In adapting man's way of life to a more suitable form from the savage to the cultivated state, and in changing his diet from crude to careful, men have acted precisely as doctors do: the method and the discovery are identical for both.

But dietotherapy does not mean simply restricting or eliminating coarse foods. If sustaining force is not found in the diet, the patient will suffer the harm of a diet inadequate to his needs. Abstention from nourishment may cause weakness, sickness, and even death. No measure or number can determine this question of adequacy; it must be sought in the reactions of the body. In each instance the habits of the individual must be considered: for some, alteration of these habits makes little or no difference. For others, it may be upsetting, if indeed it is not attended by more or less serious consequences.

From the foregoing the reader can see that the health sciences, insofar as they are concerned with nutrition and dietetics, go back at least to the author of *Ancient Medicine*. The nutritionist and the dietician can trace their professional ancestry to the Hippocratic Collection, no less than the physician, the nurse, and the pharmacist can.

The ancient writer recognized that precision of treatment is often requisite, yet, as he says, this is commonly difficult since the art of medicine does not possess such a degree of exactitude. But for him this is no reason to reject the medicine which he himself characterizes as "ancient," since one ought instead to praise it for coming as close as it can to exactitude and to admire its development of discovery by wise investigation rather than chance after a period of great ignorance.

The complexity of diet makes it very evident that the cure of disease rests on no simple hypothesis of contrasting states such as heat and cold, wetness and dryness. These are not inherent properties of the dietary means by which the patient's resistance to disease is increased.

The preparation and type of foodstuff employed in the treatment of the sick are, however, of the greatest importance. Every characteristic of the nutriment used has its effect on the body, and each contributes to the way in which life is based in health, in convalescence, and in sickness. The writer considers the successful discovery and application of such helpful diets to be of divine inspiration and the glory of medicine.

A notion, both ideal and practical, of balance underlay the author's dietary theory. According to him, the degree of strength of

every property had to be considered rather than whether that property or substance was hot, cold, wet, or dry. When these properties
are mixed and blended together and none is predominant over the
others, no ill-effect results, but when one property in particular has
the uppermost, then the system is upset and pain occurs as a result
of the undue concentration. Normal diets therefore exclude such excessive unblended components, excepting of course those de-
liberately introduced to tease or sate the appetite. Normal diets in
general use cause no difficulty; instead they contribute vigor,
growth, and nourishment to the degree that they are properly composed, with nothing unblended, nothing too strong, and to the
degree that they are single, simple, and plain.

G. E. R. Lloyd's recent book, *Polarity and Analogy: Two Types
of Argumentation in Early Greek Thought,* turns often to the Hippocratic Collection for examples of the reasoning he is interested in
exploring and gives a balanced critical judgment of the reasonable
and unreasonable in several Hippocratic essays.

The author of *Ancient Medicine* resumes his attack on the philosophical theorists who dabble in medicine by saying that those who
try to base the practice of medicine on a notion of simple causes,
like the polarities of hot and cold, or wet and dry, are bound to be
embarrassed in treating the sick, since they will not find in nature
substances that exhibit such qualities without admixture. They have
to make use of the same foods and drinks that all men use, yet they
attribute the result of their use to the hypothesized quality. They are
also in difficulty in prescribing treatment because no one else knows
or recognizes what they mean by such qualities.

The temperature-regulating mechanisms of the body were known
to the essayist only by their effects. So he says that cold and heat
have the least effect on the body when the two are tempered or
mixed together. Again, the underlying notion is balance: blending
or mixing of properties is essential for health. We may with caution
look on this as a recognition of what modern investigators have
termed "homeostasis." The ancient writer has inferred a homeostasis of complex interactions from a wealth of experience and sound
observation.

Each of the two, cold and heat, can when isolated do harm. Yet,
at the inception of cold, the body itself supplies heat without aid or
preparation. This occurs in both the well and the sick. Cold baths
in winter followed by clothing and blanketing the body produce only

warmth. Similarly, hot baths are followed by cooling of the body's own accord. The cooling of fanning is likewise followed by increased warmth, whereas the person who does not try to cool himself in this way feels no such increase. Even more striking are the heat and itching of those exposed to low temperatures for unduly long periods of time. So with the sick; chilling is accompanied by fever, and when the fever disappears with sweating, the sick man is colder than if he had not had the fever.

Two terms which recur commonly in the Hippocratic writings are *crasis* and *pepsis*. *Crasis* denotes mixing, blending, combining, or tempering. *Pepsis* is literally "cooking," for which the early translation in English has "coction," but a better term—as long as we do not assume by it the understanding of processes achieved in modern times—would be "digestion," or a process of altering or transforming by the application of heat with resultant softening, ripening, chemical change, or changes in concentration. Both *crasis* and *pepsis* are used in the next section of *Ancient Medicine* in which the nature of fevers is further analyzed.

In acute fevers the heat apparently does not alternate with cold, but this should be considered the chief proof that fever is not the simple product of heat and that heat is not the sole cause of the illness. Instead, there are bitter heats, acid heats, salty heats, and a thousand others, and there are colds too with as many different qualities. These are the real causes of sickness. In coryza or nasal catarrh, for example, acidity causes excessive heat and a burning sensation. Irritation and inflammation disappear when acidity is reduced, when the fluid thickens and mixes more with the previous flow. Where heat is quickly replaced by cold there is no need of *pepsis,* but colds produced by acidities and fluid imbalances are dispelled by *crasis* and *pepsis.*

When fluids thicken by *pepsis* and lose their acidity, fever abates and with the abatement all the distressing symptoms of the patient disappear. So the cause of each illness must be attributed to a particular combination. The illness ceases when the combination is transformed into a different mixture.

As long as the fluids are in movement without *crasis* or *pepsis,* medicine has no means to end the pain and the fever. So it is the fluids of the body with their various properties, which in the proper mixture, determine health for the individual, whereas the property of heat can diminish only through admixture with cold. The greater

the number of mixtures which the fluids of the body have undergone,
the better for the health of the individual: then everything remains
in *pepsis* and repose, with nothing displaying a predominant quality.

If there are difficulties in apprehending or following the author's
discussion at this point, and there are, the difficulties inhere in
his style and reasoning, not solely in the received text.

How medicine differs from philosophy is a subject the author returns to in chapter 20. He says that some, including physicians as
well as sophists, assert that a knowledge of medicine is impossible
without a knowledge of what man is, and that one who wishes to
practice the art of medicine intelligently must possess this know-
edge. Their discussion tends to philosophy, like that of Empedocles
(the natural philosopher of Agrigentum, 483/2–423 B.C.) and like
others who have written on man's nature, what he is in principle,
how he was first created, and how composed.

In Jones's view (Vol. I, p. 5) this passage and other internal evidence help to supply a rough date of 430–420 B.C. for the composition of *Ancient Medicine*. Such a time alone makes it conceivable,
if still uncertain, that it is genuinely the work of Hippocrates, not
just that of a Hippocratic writer.

But all this speculation we find belongs less to the art of medicine than to the art of drawing or painting. Actually, a knowledge
of man's nature can only come from medicine in its most general
application. Every doctor must study human nature and carefully
investigate, if he wishes to fulfill his obligations, the relationships
of man to his nutrition, his drink, his entire way or type of life, and
the influences which each of these has on each man. In other
words, for the physician the question of man's nature is not
philosophic—as Empedocles and others spoke of it in terms of man's
origin and composition—but is directly related to man and his external and internal environment.

The essay then concludes with a discussion of the relationships
between the bodily fluid and the bodily organs. Its final statement
is that the investigator of external conditions can successfully conduct his research and will always be able to choose the best treatment. The best treatment is that which is least unsuitable.[2]

II   Airs

Airs is included here for two reasons. First, it characterizes
medicine, though it does so as a layman might see it; second, it as-

cribes all pathology to a single "form" (*idee*) and cause, namely airs (*physai*).

This ultimate reduction of all disease to a single cause is not obviously Hippocratic. It is antithetic, at least superficially, to other Hippocratic statements in which the causation of disease is considered to be multifactorial. But we must keep in mind the author's closing statement, that air is the most active factor, others are cofactorial: contributory and accessory.

Yet the essay has its place in the collection, if not in the canon of Hippocratic writings. In spite of apparent contradictions with other writings in the Collection, it can be brought into conformity with them if it is regarded as a kind of "unified field theory" of disease. Again, the ascription of all disease to either corruption or malfunction of airs external and internal to the body seems so extravagant that the reaction of the reader ranges from "ingenious" (Adams) to "absurd" (Jones). Littré thought it a sophistic thesis which *Man's Nature* and *Ancient Medicine* were intended to refute.

The form and content of this lecture may both have been determined by the nature of the audience for whom it was intended, and a physician might introduce simplifications and a point of view which would appeal to laymen. It was, in fact, the author of *Ancient Medicine* who wrote that the subject of medical inquiry is the pains and sufferings of ordinary human beings and that if the expert fails to be understood by laymen he also fails to achieve reality (chapter 2).

The overriding importance of the work is that the author has so well understood the fact that air is essential to life. He tells us that the character (*tropos*) of all diseases is the same but that the locus or site (*topos*) varies. Variation in site induces the belief that diseases have no similarity to each other. There is, however, a single form and cause of all disease. All living beings are nourished by three types of nutriment: solids, liquids, and air (*pneuma*). The distinction between *physa* and *pneuma* is that the current in bodies is called breath (*physa*), but outside bodies it is called air (*pneuma*)—a distinction not observed in other parts of the Collection.

The power of air is the greatest of all in all things. Air in violent motion is capable of uprooting trees, producing waves on the sea, and flinging about ships of enormous size. Nothing can exist without air, and it is everywhere present, invisible to the sight but apparent to the reason.

Everything between heaven and earth is filled with air. Air is the cause of seasonal variation, thick and cold in winter, gentle and calm in summer. Even the progression of sun, moon, and stars is due to air. Air is the food of fire: fire without air could not exist. That the sea too partakes of air is evident, for marine animals could never exist without air, since they partake of air in no other way than by drawing it from the water in which they subsist. Even the earth is a solid base (*bathron*) for air; air is the vehicle (*ochema*) of earth; and nothing is empty of air.

Air is the cause of life. It is indispensable to life, and it is responsible for diseases in the sick. A man may be deprived of everything else, both solid food as well as drink, for as much as two, three, or even more days, and yet survive; however, if the air passages into the body are cut off, a man would die in a fraction of a day, since the body's greatest need is for air.

The question, of course, is the relevance of this not unreasonable thesis to specific diseases. We must not expect to find in his discussion information and understanding only recently won in modern times by pathophysiology, chemistry, and anatomy. Some commentators in modern times have shown great chagrin or embarrassment over the apparent shortcomings of the Hippocratic writers in these areas. In particular, W. H. S. Jones reacted strongly to such deficiencies. It is of course disappointing that we cannot at all times compare ancient and modern favorably. It is really a compliment to the ancient writers or an indication of the strong impression they make on us generally that our expectations of them are usually and justifiably high. The higher the expectation, the more severe the disappointment, if it appears that the reality was less than good.

Instead, I think that what should be emphasized here is that the author in this instance repeatedly shows his grasp of the essential facts such as careful observation could elicit, the most important of which is that respiratory embarrassment and respiratory failure are involved in crucial ways in the very diseases which he discusses, and that his recognition of the importance of air to health cannot really be challenged. Further, none of the clinical descriptions of disease could have been drawn by a mere sophist. The writer was not only a physician but an excellent one, if we judge solely by the accuracy *for his times* of the statements he makes and the acumen of his inferential judgments.

A list of the diseases which he discusses will give an idea of the range of pathology with which he was familiar. Symptoms are not always distinguished from the diseases. First, he mentions fevers (as a "disease" associated with all other diseases), whether they are epidemic or sporadic; flatus; shivering in fevers; ileus (or bowel obstructions); flatulent colic (*aneilemmata*); chest hemorrhages; belching; discharges (fluxes, flows, or rheums: *rheumata*); sore throats, eyes, or ears; coughing; flesh lacerations; dropsy; apoplexy; epilepsy; and in general disturbed states where conscious awareness is interfered with (even sleep reveals the essential involvement of air by the lowered respiration, lowered temperature of the body); the alteration of conscious awareness and the persistence in altered form called dreams of different notions (*doxai heterai*); drunkenness; and mental aberrations. In epilepsy, the seizure ends when circulation of blood and air is restored and calm is re-established. It should be noted here that the description of epilepsy in *Airs* is in agreement with the statements made in *The Sacred Disease Epilepsy,* particularly in chapters 7, 10, 19 and 20.

There are many excellent and interesting statements made in *Airs,* and as far as space permits they deserve mention here.

One kind of fever is epidemic and called plague (*loimos*). The other type is sporadic and attacks those whose regime is poor. But both types are caused by air. Epidemic fever exists because men inhale the same air. When a like air is mixed in like fashion with the body, the fevers too are alike. If only one species of animal is affected, it is because bodies differ from each other, as airs differ from each other, one nature from another, and one nutriment from another. Thus variation in response to infection reflects the variation in species and their concomitant varieties of susceptibility to the causative agents.

Trembling of the body in chills is caused as follows: the blood "in fear" of the present chill collects rapidly and rushes throughout the body to the warmest parts. As the blood drains from the extremities into the viscera, the extremities begin to tremble. The parts depleted of blood are bound to tremble because of the resultant chill, from the loss of their heat. Those parts engorged with blood tremble precisely because of the added amount of blood. Yawning precedes fevers because considerable amounts of air are massed together and it forces its way up and through the mouth, which provides it with ready passage. (The author compares this process to steam rising from a pot of boiling water.)

Headaches accompanied by fever have this cause: narrowing develops in the passages of the blood in the head because the veins are filled with air, which in turn produces the headache, for the blood which is hot and violently forced through narrow passage cannot get through them quickly owing to the many hindrances and barriers in its way. For the same reason, pulsations develop around the temples. In ileus (bowel obstruction) and flatulent colic, the obvious cause is the settling of air, since the treatment of such cases is to remove the air. Sometimes the hypochondria (abdomen) are affected, sometimes the flanks, sometimes both. The therapy therefore is to attempt to reduce the pain by external application of heat. The reason for this is that heat which is externally applied draws the air and makes it pass through the body, with resultant alleviation to some degree of the pain.

So with hemorrhages in the chest cavity. The blood, surcharged with air in the veins of the head, eventually reaches other parts of the body, and wherever it masses it causes a disease, signalized by local pain (in the eyes, ears, throat, etc.). When it spreads to the chest, the acrid phlegm ulcerates the vessels and disrupts the veins. The extravasated blood decays with time into pus as it is incapable of rising or descending, since fluids have difficulty in rising and the diaphragm prevents its descent.

Nothing in the body contributes more to conscious reflection than the blood. As long as the blood remains stable, conscious reflection is stable also. But when the blood composition is altered, conscious reflection also changes for the worse. If then all the blood is disturbed, conscious reflection is completely suppressed or destroyed.

Air, combining throughout the body with all the blood, causes the sacred disease (epilepsy). Numerous points of congestion then develop in the veins everywhere. The impeded blood fails to pass or else irregularities are introduced which affect and reduce its free passage. Convulsions result from these irregularities, for the whole body is dragged in all directions; twisting of all kinds develops in every possible way. Throughout the duration of the seizure, those affected are insensible to every external stimulus, they are deaf to what is said, blind to what happens around them, and unaffected by pain. Such is the effect of a disturbance of air on the blood which it pollutes. Foam naturally is discharged at the mouth. This is the product of air passing through the veins, which then rises and brings with it the thinnest of the blood. The resultant mixture of air and moisture turns white, for the air being pure is discerned through the thinness (of the exudate.)

The epileptic seizure ends when the body has warmed the blood through its exertions and the warmed blood in turn warms the air. When the air is thoroughly warmed and carried away, the congested blood relaxes, some of the air being discharged with the breath, some with the phlegm. The froth ends, the blood is restored to normal, and calm reappears in the body.

Air is the most active factor throughout all diseases. Everything else is a contributory and accessory cause (*alla panta synaitia kai metaitia*).

The writer's description of medicine comes at the beginning of *Airs*. There are arts, he says, which are full of difficulty for those who have acquired them, but beneficial to those who make use of them. They are a general blessing to ordinary persons but painful for those who practice them. Among such arts is the one which the Greeks call *ietrike* (medicine). The explanation of this is that the physician sees terrible things, handles unpleasant things, and suffers from the misfortunes of others griefs which are peculiar to him.

Thanks to this art of medicine the sick recover from the greatest evils: disease, pain, suffering, and the threat of death. Medicine is found to be the healer of all these afflictions.

The defects of this art of medicine are hard to determine; it is simpler to determine the virtues. Only doctors can know the defects of the art; laymen cannot. The reason for this is that the doctor's actions are not of the body but of the understanding. Whenever surgery is indicated, habitual practice is necessary because practice is the best trainer of the hands. But judgment concerning the most obscure and difficult diseases is much more dependent on opinion than on art or skill. In such instances, there is the greatest possible difference between experience and inexperience. Of such instances one of great consequence certainly is this, namely, what is the cause of diseases, and what is the beginning and source of the pathological states of the body. Obviously, if a person knows the cause of the disease, he would be able to apply the beneficial procedures. In fact, this kind of medicine is most in keeping with nature. For example, hunger is a disease, for whatever distresses man is called disease. Well, what is the remedy for hunger? Whatever puts an end to hunger, namely food. So hunger must be cured by food. Similarly, in the case of drink which cures thirst, fullness by emptying, emptiness by filling up, and exhaustion by inactivity. In short, the opposites are cures for their opposites.

The last sentence in *Airs* shows the author's insight as well as his ability to summarize his views: medicine is removal and addition, the removal of excess, and the addition of what is lacking and needed. Whoever best achieves these is the best physician; the practitioner who fails most in achieving these is the one who fails most in the art as well.

III   The Art of Medicine

The Art of Medicine (Peri technes) is a carefully and at times beautifully written brief defense of medicine as a real, existent, practical, and beneficial art of the possible. It may be part of a larger work since chapter 9 has the statement "another time and another discussion will treat of other arts." It has an interesting preamble with a sharp and witty attack on those who "make an art of disparaging the arts." Such persons only show their malice and lack of art.

Following the preamble is a section in which the writer argues somewhat platonically for the existence of all arts that "no art exists which is not seen as the result of some *form*." "Form" in Jones's translation becomes "real essence," and Littré (Vol. 6, p. 5) uses "réalité." Elsewhere, in another context, Jones translates the term *eidos* by "reality," but though he does so, he thinks the meaning(s) of "form" and "face" are not excluded.[3] Perhaps what is meant here is "visible entity." In other words, that which is visible exists; the arts are visible and they therefore exist. They even take their names from their *forms*.

The essay proper begins with a definition of medicine. Medicine has a three-fold purpose: (1) to alleviate the sufferings of the sick; (2) to reduce the severity of their illnesses; and (3) *not* to treat those who are overcome by their illnesses, in the knowledge that this is beyond the scope and power of the practice of medicine.[4]

It should be noted that the first two purposes given by the writer are mutually complementary. More important, the conservativeness of the definition is remarkable. Medicine is not defined as we might define it today, as the art of healing, or in a more detailed fashion as "the science and art concerned with the cure, alleviation, and prevention of disease, and with the restoration and preservation of health," as it is defined in the *Oxford Universal Dictionary* (1955 edition). The twentieth edition of *Stedman's Medical Dictionary* (1961), instead of combining the "science and art" as a unity, dichotomizes them, as "the art of preventing or curing disease" and, secondly, as "the science that treats of disease in all its relations." But the reason for the dichotomy is scarcely apparent.

The essayist who composed *The Art of Medicine* has made a striking advance in this purposeful definition of medicine over the vagueness of the term *ietrike,* which is simply "art of healing." The essayist shows greater insight and judgment, and he puts first what he is convinced must come first, the alleviation of suffering, *then* the reduction of severity of illness. And how strong the feeling was in the school of medicine to which the writer belonged that intractable illness is beyond the scope of medicine is shown by its inclusion as the third and last purpose of medicine. In a sense, negative as it is, it has no place in the definition. It just does not belong. In another sense, it is the perfect complement to the notion that medicine's end and aim are simply the alleviation of human suffering in the ill and the reduction of the severity of their illnesses. Medicine is thus defined, from a qualitative point of view, conservatively, restrictively, and exclusively with regard to its appropriate sphere of operation (which is illness) and its purpose (which is the alleviation of symptoms in *tractable* diseases). Of course, the exclusion of intractable disease from the purview of medicine is not original with either the essayist or the Greeks, since it is often instanced in Egyptian medicine and is in fact a striking feature of it.

There is a remarkable return to this definition of medicine in a modern work by Walter Modell, called *Relief of Symptoms,* the second edition of which appeared in 1961. He writes: "The keystone of modern medicine is etiologic diagnosis and therapy—the determination of causes of diseases and their eradication through specifics. . . . The oddly contemptuous contemporary attitude toward the relief of symptoms is largely the consequence of the modern revolution in therapeutic aim. In a single generation advances in medicine have made the cure the goal, indeed often the rule, whereas formerly symptom relief was the best the physician could hope for as the direct result of his efforts."[5]

In chapter 6 of *The Art of Medicine* the writer states that his argument that medicine is an art would be weak if cures were achieved only by drugs, and in chapter 7 we have his statement that "the patient wants treatment in order to get prompt relief of symptoms rather than to recover his health."[6]

The definition of medicine which he gave is consistent with the wording of the famous *Oath,* in which the practitioner is spoken of as one who "uses treatment to help the sick" and who "enters the house to help the sick."

The remainder of *The Art* is an elaboration of the contention that medicine exists as a practical and beneficial art and a defense of it against those who attribute all its success to luck and who censure it for its failures, especially for its failure to help the desperately ill.

His answer to the first criticism is that although luck may be involved, the wisdom and experience of the practitioner reduce the element of uncertainty. This argument is further supported by the reasonable observation that luck is only the appearance on the surface of the subsurface working of hidden but logical causes. Mistakes as well as successful treatment attest the existence of the art since right and wrong, benefit and harm, are appropriate to every art.

It is also more likely, he says, that the patient will fail to carry out the doctor's orders than that the orders themselves will be wrong, so that the blame for lack of success is often mistakenly placed upon the practitioner. Again, if the prescribed treatment fails, the blame should attach to the strength of the disease and not to the art of the physician.

So, too, with desperate cases: their treatment is beyond the reach of medicine. The limitations of the art must be recognized as fairly and honestly as would be done in the case of any other art. This has for us a bearing on the modern problem of euthanasia in hopeless cases.

The obscurity of the workings of the inner organs requires all the more effort and time on the part of the practitioner. Though obscure, they can still be mastered insofar as the patient can be examined and the investigator can pursue his research. Suffering because of the difficulty of quick observation is not the physician's fault but arises from the nature of the patient and his ailment.

Treatment will follow a reasonable and gentle course only when the art is clearly aware of the requisite information. Often disease has the advantage over treatment in that its beginnings are obscure and hidden from sight. To this may be added the negligence of the sick: they come for help only when the disease has established itself. The contributory cause, to be sure, is their ignorance: they simply do not know what is wrong with them. Even though the internal processes of disease may be hidden, still the practitioner is enormously aided by the external signs and symptoms as well as by those interventions which force nature to surrender her secrets without harm to the patient (chapter 13).

Chapter 10, on internal diseases, is the most physiological part of the discussion. Diseases affecting the bones and the cavities are by their nature hidden from direct observation. All the limbs are wrapped in flesh which is called muscle (*mys*). Every discontinuous process in the body, whether covered by skin or flesh, is hollow. In health the hollow is filled with breath (*pneuma*). In disease the hollow is filled with a sero-purulent matter (*ichor*). All the parts are porous, all are encircled by cells, the presence of which is shown by the serum, which comes out in quantity when the cells are opened, causing great pain. The term used here for "cells" is *thalamai*.

Chapter 11, which is concerned with the difficulties of treatment when the causes of the illness are obscure, underscores the inevitable ignorance of the patient and his inability to report accurately, so that those who look after him have increased need for accurate observation and assessment or evaluation of what they themselves see and hear. As I have shown elsewhere, it is at least probable that the "attendants" (*hoi therapeuontes*) are either medical students or male nurses left in charge by the physician. Other passages in the Collection are even more definitive of this probability.[7] They are *not* to be thought of as licensed practical nurses, ward attendants, or orderlies.

That the *Art of Medicine* is not the work of a practitioner of the art and that it is the work of a sophist (Protagoras according to Theodor Gomperz, Hippias according to W.H.S. Jones) seem to me improbable hypotheses based on undemonstrated preconceptions about the style of the essay. Jones found "the rhetorical character ... so striking that without doubt it must be attributed to a sophist. The elaborate parallels, verbal antitheses, and balancing of phrase with phrase, can have no other explanation."[8] There is, however, in the literary finish of the product, nothing which compels the conclusion I have quoted.

IV   Regimen, Book I (Peri diaites to proton)

Regimen I is a very diverse work, often philosophic and speculative, loosely held together by the proposal to treat of the relationship of a prescribed manner of living (or, "regimen") to health among human beings. The work may be divided into four parts. An introductory passage, composed of chapters 1 and 2, discusses the work of earlier writers in summary fashion and the author's own proposed contribution to the subject of human care. The second part, chapters 3–11, consists of speculative judgments of far-ranging nature on the nature of living things, including man. Chapters 12–24 are a demonstration of the thesis that all the arts have a common share in human nature. The statement with which this section of the work begins is, "I shall however show that the arts clearly resemble the conditions of mankind, both those conditions which are visible and those which are not. The art of foretelling the future is one such example."[9] The thesis is supported by examples drawn from a dozen different arts.

The fourth part of *Regimen I,* chapters 25–36, relates the speculative judgments of the second part to man's soul and body in a variety of ways, including rates of growth at various ages, sex determination at conception, the nature of maleness and femaleness, how twins are conceived and why, "superfetation" (a type of miscarriage), the sensitivity of response to stimuli in the individual or the lack of it and its relationship to native intelligence, as well as the appropriate regimen for various types of individuals assuming a particular constitution or constellation of determining factors. The complexity of the book is apparent from this program of topics. It seems best to consider the four parts in the sequence adopted by the author.

Part I.   Introduction

The introduction has the familiar purpose of distinguishing the writer's contribution from that made by his predecessors. No previous writer on the subject of the relationship of regimen to health has, he says, correctly understood how the subject must be treated. Partial success has been achieved but not with the whole subject matter. The writer's declared intention to indicate the extent of his agreement with earlier statements on the same subject is not carried out directly in this book, but he does intend to explain matters whose explanation has never been attempted before (chapter 1). (*Regimen* is actually a work in four books, the last of which deals with dreams. Only Book I of *Regimen* is considered in the present discussion.)

Anyone who proposes to discuss correctly the subject of human regimen must first be well acquainted with the nature of man generally. In addition, he must know the effects produced by each component of the diet. Since diet alone does not produce health, provision must also be made in the regimen for exercise, which consumes food. Work and exertion must be in turn adapted to the age, the strength, and the constitution of the individual, and in general to every conceivable factor which may operate in the individual's milieu. This includes the seasonal changes, variations in wind and weather, the location in which the patient lives, and so on. Accurate prescription is limited by the impossibility of the physician's being in constant attendance on his patient. Excess or deficiency in any component will lead to disease which can be predicted. Diseases do not strike suddenly, but develop gradually to the point where they begin to erupt. The writer claims to have uncovered the signs and symptoms which indicate the development of the disease process and the means by which a healthy state can be restored.

Part II.   The Composition of Living Beings

All living things, including man, are composed of two different but cooperating substances: fire and water. It is the interplay of these two cardinal elements which accounts for the universe as we know it, both the microcosm and the macrocosm. The attributes of the two elements are discussed. The following are among the more significant statements in chapters 12–24:

Nothing is destroyed of all existent things, and nothing is created which did not exist before. (This may be the first medical statement of the conservation of matter.)

Change in things occurs when they are mixed together or separated. This is the judgment of the mind, whereas the majority of men are deceived by the judgment of the eyes. Yet the eyes alone are incapable of judgment.

"Becoming" and "dying" are popular terms. They really refer to "combination" and "separation." The fact is that combination and separation are the same thing, as are "growth" and "decay."

All things, both human and divine, are in flux, changing ceaselessly up and down.

The author describes an intricate interaction between the elements of fire and water which eventually produces in man bones, sinews, "hollow veins," and flesh.

His description of the belly is remarkably poetic: the belly is the largest part, in charge of dry as well as moist water, giving to all and taking from all, a power of the sea, nurse of suitable creatures, destroyer of unsuitable creatures. It is surrounded by a combination of cold and moist water, with a passage for cold and warm breath. It is a model of the earth which transforms everything which falls into it.

Men do not understand how to examine the invisible on the basis of the visible. Although the arts of men resemble the nature of man, men do not recognize this. The mind of the gods taught them to imitate their own nature, yet though they know what they are doing, they do not know what they are imitating.

Though unlike, all things are alike.

The arrangements of men, right or wrong, never remain constant, whereas the arrangements of the gods are always right.

Part III.   The Relationship of the Arts to Man's Experience

The arts (a term which includes for us the referential meanings of skills, crafts, occupations, and professions) visibly resemble the experience, both visible and invisible, of man. (I have used the broader term "experience" to represent the range of meaning of the Greek term *pathemata,* for which both Littré and Jones adopted the word "affections," but the latter in modern English would be unduly ambiguous in this context.)

The arts chosen by the author to demonstrate this visible resemblance to human experience are common enough in Greek culture of the day: prophecy, ironworking, clothes cleaning, shoe repair, carpentry, building, musical harmony, cooking, currying, goldworking, sculpture, pottery, writing, and athletic training. In each art, there are elements of resemblance to man's experience and, in sum, all the arts partake of the nature of man (chapter 24).

One example, of shoe repair, will indicate the writer's analogical thinking: decay in men's bodies is healed by the physician through stitching and cutting (there is, evidently, no restriction here on surgery as an integral part of medicine). This also belongs to medicine, as it seeks to remove the cause of pain and make the patient well.

From the same passage comes the notion, variously expressed elsewhere, that nature itself possesses healing power and so resembles the art of the physician (*he physis automate tauta epistatai,* nature of its own accord understands these things—and knows how to achieve them, for which we have the equivalent Latin phrase *Naturae vis medicatrix,* the curative force of Nature).

Part IV. Man's Soul and Man's Body

The concluding section of *Regimen I* (chapters 25–36) relates the hypothecated polarities of fire and water, moist and dry, to a broad range of topics, beginning with the human soul.

THE SOUL. The growth of the soul, which is a blend of the elements of fire and water, corresponds to the age of the individual: in youth, as the body grows, the soul's revolution (*periphore*) is swift, and the soul catches fire, thins out, and is consumed for the body's growth. In more mature bodies, the motion is reduced, and the body itself is cold, so that the soul is consumed for the diminution of the individual. Bodies at the peak of their development and at the age of procreation can nourish and develop the soul.

SEX DIFFERENTIATION. Females are more inclined to water and will develop from food, drink, and activities which are cold, moist, and gentle.

Males incline more to fire and will develop from food and regimen which are dry and warm.

If female offspring is desired, a watery regimen must be used. Conversely, if male offspring is desired, a fiery regimen must be used. Both parents must use the same regimen.

On one day in each month the fire can solidify and dominate the advancing water, provided that the parts from both parents coincide in place.

If the substances secreted from both parents are male, the offspring will be male, with a brilliant soul and strong body, unless his subsequent regimen is harmful.

Variation in masculinity and feminity is determined by the contribution of each parent, whichever is dominant. If the woman secretes the male substance and the man secretes the female substance, bisexual or androgynous offspring are produced, assuming the dominance of the male substance.

So three kinds of individual males are produced, but masculinity (virility) is related to the blending of the parts of water, as well as to subsequent nutrition, training, and habits.

The same theory is used to explain female sex and femininity.

TWINS. The character of the uterus is the chief cause of twin births. The uterus must be able to give nourishment equally to both fetuses on both of its sides. Male twins are produced when both parents have male secretions. When the secretions are sexually different, the dominant secretion determines the sex of the twins.

The similarity of twins results from the sameness of the fetal environment, their original conjoint secretion, and their birth at the same time (chapter 31).

SUPERFETATION. Superfetation (*epigonon*) is the supposed conception of a second embryo some time after the first is conceived. The author attributes the occurrence of an extra embryo to a natural heat and dryness of the womb and the woman, as well as that of the entering seed. Such superfetation eventually results in the aborting of both fetuses since the same things are unsuitable for them (chapter 31). (The notion of "superfetation" may have been inspired by observation of difference in development of multiple fetuses in abortion cases, but most likely goes back to a much earlier idea that conception is possible from successive inseminations by one or more males.)

AGE AND HEALTH. The health of the individual is related to his age but in turn depends on the original constitution or mixture of fire and water. In general, the males of all species are warmer and drier, the females moister and colder, for two reasons: their original constitution and their postnatal regimen (chapters 32–34.)

MENTAL APTITUDE. The author's term for "mental aptitude" is *phronesis*. This includes intellection, or faculty of reasoning, and the sensitivity to sensory and abstract stimuli. The seat of intellection is the soul.

The greatest mental aptitude results from the mixture in the individual of the moistest fire and the driest water.

If the fire has less force than the water, the soul so endowed is necessarily slower and such individuals are called foolish (moronic?). The senses are quick but the circuit in such instances is slow with resultant spasmodic meeting between sense and sense object. But proper regimen can help even these persons.

However, the mixture of fire and water does not cause quick temper, laziness, deception, simplicity, hostility, or friendliness. These are instead determined by the character of the passages through which the soul goes. Regimen cannot alter these traits since it is impossible to alter the form of invisible nature.

The character of the voice is analogously determined by the passages through which the air goes and what it encounters.

Taken together, we have in this concluding portion of *Regimen I* an early and often naive-sounding psychology, yet one in which the modern reader can observe startling similarities in rough outline to notions and theories new or current in our own time, and some elements among them retain a fascination and attractiveness for the speculatively inclined, however elusive may be the terms, shifting and ambiguous to a degree, in which the author has stated them.

V The Nature of Man (Peri physios anthropou)

The Nature of Man is a relatively short work and the apparent remaining source of the humoral theory which persisted into modern times as a dominant conception of man's physical nature. Ben Jonson's *Everyman in His Humour* (published in 1598) is the outstanding example of the penetration of the humoral theory into literature.

Chapters 1–3 form a refutation of the monistic views of man's nature. The body has, in fact, many components which by faulty interaction cause disease. Diseases themselves are many in form (type?), and their cure is likewise complex. Those who say that man is only blood or only bile or only phlegm are therefore quite mistaken.

Humoral Theory

According to the author of this influential work, the human body is composed of four humors or fluid substances: blood, phlegm, yellow bile, and black bile. These four humors determine the nature of the body as well as the states of health and disease. Perfect health exists when the four humors display a balanced proportion to each other in respect to their combination, strength, and quantity, and when all four are most properly combined. Pain results from either a deficiency or excess of any one of these fluids or from the failure of any one of them to combine with the other fluids.

The four humors or body fluids are differentiated by their color, their evident tactile difference, their degrees of warmth or cold, and their differences in dryness and moisture.

Phlegm is the coldest and most viscid of the four humors. It increases in quantity in wintertime, whereas blood increases in spring and summer. Phlegm is weakest in summer. There are seasonal variations in all the humors. There is also a direct correspondence in all four humors to the temperature and humidity of the four seasons.

The principles of *therapy* are based on cure by opposites ("allopathy"). For example, diseases which are caused by excess must be cured by reduction, diminution, or evacuation. Diseased states resulting from exertion are to be cured by rest; those caused by inactivity are curable by activity, work, or exercise. This makes it requisite that the physician know the varieties of disease, the characteristic constitutions of men, of seasons, and of ages.

Disease is caused by defects in regimen or by the air we breathe. The statement is not contradictory but complementary to others made in the same work.) Epidemics are airborne, whereas a multiplicity of different diseases in a given area is evidence of a defect in the regimen of those individuals affected. In epidemics the patient should be isolated as far as possible from the sources of infection (chapter 9).

The more serious diseases are those which affect the dominant or strongest parts of the body (here argument and observation seem to complement one another most plausibly). Diseases which arise, however, in the weaker parts of the body and move from them to the stronger parts will be offset by the greater ability of the stronger parts to overcome immigrant humors. (Thus, diseases may be said to be "humor-borne".)

The four thickest *veins* (i.e., arteries, for which the Greek is *phlebes,* or veins) are paired. One pair extends from behind the head all the way to the feet, descending from the neck through either side of the spine. A second pair, the jugular "veins," lead from the head by the ears through the neck, descending on either side of the spine to the testicles and thighs, reaching the ankles and feet by way of the popliteal space behind the knees. The third pair reach from the temples to the anus, via the shoulder blades, lungs, spleen, kidneys, and liver. The fourth pair extend from the forehead and eyes to the genitals, by way of the neck, collar bones, arms, armpits, spleen, liver, and belly. The body is nourished by a complex network of veins of all kinds which originate in the belly. (Needless to say, a puzzling scramble of internal anatomy!)

Most *fevers* originate in the bile (chapter 15). Leaving aside those which accompany other diseases and wounds, there are four types of cholagenic fevers: unremitting, quotidian, tertian, and quartan (the malarial fevers). The stubbornness of quartan fever is caused by black bile, the most viscous of the body humors. Quartan fevers occur chiefly in autumn in patients who are between their twenty-fifth and forty-fifth years.

Such is the work which left us with the humoral theory down to the seventeenth century.

VI Body Fluids (Peri chymon)

Unlike the other essays we have discussed in this chapter, *Body Fluids* has no organized or discursively examined theory to present. The title of this essay is a misnomer and comes apparently from the opening sentence.[10] The first words of the essay are: "The color of the humors (body fluids), when undiluted, resembles that of flowers." The text following this phrase is, however, uncertain. The work is listed under the title *Peri chymon,* which is sometimes translated as *On Humors* by the ancient commentators Bacchius, Celsus, and Erotian.

Bacchius (in Greek, Bakcheios) was a native of Tanagra (now Grimadha) in Boeotia and lived about 200 B.C. He was a physician and follower of the brilliant Chalcedonian Herophilus, who was the pupil of Praxagoras of Cos, an early third-century physician who resided in Alexandria and was the discoverer of the rhythm of the pulse, as well as first dissector in public of the body.

Bacchius wrote a commentary on Book VI of the *Epidemics,* and another on *Aphorisms* and *The Clinic,* all of them parts of the Hippocratic Collection. He also edited *Epidemics III* and composed a work in three books called *Lexeis,* a glossary of difficult and obsolete terms in the Hippocratic Collection. The latter was the first work of its kind on the Collection and apparently was analphabetic.[11] A considerable number of brief fragments of this lexicon has survived.

Aulus Cornelius Celsus, contemporary of the Roman emperor

Tiberius, was an encyclopedist and lay author of eight extant books on medicine. It was Celsus who said of Hippocrates that he was the "first who separated medicine from philosophy."

Peri chymon was rejected as apocryphal by Heraclides of Tarentum (c.75 B.C.),"the most important empirical physician of antiquity," as he is described by William David Ross.

One of the few surviving medical works of antiquity outside the Hippocratic Collection itself is the *Glossary* of Erotian which was intended to illuminate the language of the Hippocratic Collection. It is the source, incidentally, of the oldest known methodically arranged listing of the Hippocratic writings and contains comments on the authenticity of several works in the Collection. Erotian dedicated his *Glossary* to Andromachus as *archiatros* (chief physician) and personal physician of the emperor Nero.

The real subjects of *Body Fluids* are diseases, their causes, symptomatology, and treatment. Only those statements which are theoretical or imply a theory of health are given below. (Arabic numerals refer to chapters of the Greek text.)

The symptoms (semeia) which help the patient are quite similar (presumably, to each other), as are those which cause harm. In making one's calculations, the symptoms which are more numerous are more important and more severe; those which indicate recovery are more important than the others (chapter 4). All symptoms which are dangerous must be averted or combated (chapter 4).

The character of the ailment should be considered on the basis of the secretions in the first phases of the disease, the condition of the urine, the nature of the onset, any change in color, or embarrassment in breathing, along with the other symptoms (chapter 5).

All the critical signs resemble one another, both the beneficial and the harmful, as well as the destructive ones (chapter 5—a restatement of notion expressed in chapter 4). Body wastes are significant not by their amount but by the degree to which they conform to the norm and the patient's ability to tolerate them. (chapter 6). If pain develops at any point before illness is apparent, this is where the fluids settle.

Coughs, like fevers, cause abscessions (*apostasies*) or suppurative inflammation (chapter 7). Jones defined "abscession" in the following way: "When the morbid residue failed to be normally evacuated, it was gathered together to one part of the body and eliminated, sometimes as an eruption or inflammation, sometimes as a gangrene or tumour, sometimes as a swelling at the joints."[12]

One must know the seasons in which fluids erupt, the types of illnesses they cause, and the kinds of symptoms they produce in each illness. As for the individual in general, one must know the disease to which the individual's nature most inclines (chapter 8).

Psychic symptoms include intemperance in drinking and eating, sleep, wakefulness, and the regular or irregular endurance of exertion either because of some passion (like playing dice) or because of one's occupation (craft) or because of necessity, as well as changes from one type to another (chapter 9).

The emotional states of fears, shame, pain, pleasure, anger, and the like, involve the corresponding action of the appropriate part of the body, including for example sweating, cardiac palpitation, and so on (chapter 9).

The breasts, semen, and uterus are symptomatic at various ages (chapter 10). The testicles are involved in choking and coughing (chapter 10). The stomach in animals is the analogue of earth to trees: it nourishes, warms, and cools. In their ages animals resemble the year and its seasons: they do not wear out but improve with moderate use (chapter 11).

Disease typology: some diseases are congenital and are to be known by inquiry, as are those which are endemic. Others result from the individual constitution, from regimen, from the character of the disease, or from the seasons. Regions poorly situated for the seasons produce diseases imitative of those seasons (chapter 12).

Chapters 12–19 explore the relationship of seasons to disease in much detail. The best statement of this relationship is made in chapter 15: Change is especially productive of illnesses and in particular the greatest change, including the marked changes in the seasons and other things as well. However, seasons which develop gradually are the safest. This is true also of gradual changes in regimen, cold, and warmth, and the successive periods of life.

Individual constitutions may be well or poorly adapted to the seasons, some of them to summer, some to winter; again, others may be well or poorly adapted to regions, periods of life, and regimen, and to diseases of various kinds. The same is true for the various periods of life, in their adaptation to regions, seasons, regimen, and diseases of various kinds. As a result, the regimen varies with the seasons, including what we eat and drink. Activity is restricted in winter for example, and foods are kept ripe and simple, and this is important. In autumn men are energetic and much in the sun, drinking is frequent, and foods are varied with wines and fruits (chapter 16).

VII *Summary*

Taking the six works discussed in this chapter as a group, the dominant and major ideas in them may be put as follows:

(1) Medicine originated in the need for dietary regulation in the changing states of sickness and health.

(2) Medicine is necessary and beneficial, but it requires experience, knowledge, and wisdom on the part of the practitioner.

(3) Simple substances not existent in nature cannot be considered as reasonable bases for medical practice nor as an explanation of man's nature.

(4) Observation and research are requisite to the expansion of medical knowledge and improvement of medical care.

(5) All living things are nourished by solids, liquids, and air. Of these three, air is the most powerful. It is the most active factor in all disease processes, all others being contributory or accessory when compared to air.

(6) Medicine exists to alleviate the sufferings of the sick.

(7) Medical practice is determined by knowledge of man's nature.

(8) No existing thing is destroyed or created.

(9) Change in things is based on their mixture or separation.

(10) Change is constant and unending.

(11) Two different but cooperating substances account for the composition of all living things, including man: these are fire and water.

(12) Medicine is an art which corresponds, as do other human arts, to man's experience and suffering.

(13) The soul is the seat of intellectual activity or intellection.

(14) The human body is composed of four fluid substances: blood, phlegm, yellow bile, and black bile.

(15) Perfect health is the result of a balanced proportion to one another of the four fluids.

(16) Excess or deficiency or imperfect mixture of the four fluids results in pain, sickness, and disease.

(17) The principle of therapy is cure by opposites.

(18) Disease also results from defects in regimen or the air we breathe.

(19) The greatest changes, whether they occur in seasons, temperature, periods of life, or regimen, are those most likely to cause disease.

Each of the above ideas has left its mark on the development of rational medicine from the fifth century B.C. down to the modern times. Some have been discredited by the modern evolution of medical knowledge and practice. Some remain and will remain as touchstones of good medicine in all times and places. It was a very great achievement of Greek medicine to work out so much of a theory and philosophy of medicine in the less than two hundred years (and possibly in as little as a hundred) in which these six essays were composed.[13]

CHAPTER 3

The Medical Practitioner and His Profession

Medicus: vir bonus medendi peritus

(The doctor: a good man, skilled at healing)

THE figure of the doctor of medicine or physician is one of great interest and fascination, both for doctors themselves who may be inspired in their work by some ideal of the doctor or else some actual doctors who serve others as models of their profession, and for laymen as well who have a natural awe or respect for the figure of the healer in addition to the compelling need which they experience recurrently in their lives for the doctor's services. Very few laymen, in fact, are proof against the special position in society reserved for those who practice medicine. I do not mean to say that doctors are by their position automatically exempt from criticism. Hardly. In fact, public criticism of the profession has, as we know from the Hippocratic Collection itself, always existed, even inevitably, and there is more of it widespread today in our sometimes hypercritical times than ever before.

Self-criticism on the part of doctors is familiar to those acquainted with the Hippocratic Collection. It is usually coupled with self-defense, not unnaturally. And both to the observer appear healthful and helpful. The Hippocratic writers were at considerable pains to make of their art and knowledge a profession and a practice which would justify itself to man.

Though times change and knowledge multiplies beyond the grasp of single individuals, the reader will see from the works discussed in this chapter that little change in the public and professional views of the practice of medicine has taken place since the role of the practitioner was formulated twenty-four centuries ago. Even where the *practice* has changed or deviates in its own philosophy from that of the Hippocratics, the *views* tend to remain the same.

The reason for this is found in the ideal concept of "doctoring" which, in many parts of the Hippocratic Collection, received an expression since unsurpassed for clarity, vision, and—in the best sense—altruism, the unselfish self-dedication of the practitioner to the needs of his fellow men.

We like to dwell with acerbity at times on the shortcomings of individual doctors. The writers of the Hippocratic Collection often do so but in a general way and without acerbity. They have a concern for the good image of their profession. They have also the frank awareness that the good image must reflect a good reality. So their remarks are often directed to "leavening the lump."

It is remarkable to one acquainted with both areas of discussion how much the so-called ideal doctor of the Hippocratics resembles the ideal orator to which Cato and Cicero gave expression in the phrase *orator vir bonus dicendi peritus* (the ideal speaker is a good man skilled at speaking).[1] What emerges from the Hippocratic Collection is the notion that the ideal physician is a *vir bonus medendi peritus* (a good man skilled at healing).

It seems inevitable, after the fact of its elaboration, that any ideal concept of any profession would single out the two essential ingredients of *goodness* and *skill*. The former is psychological and relates to disposition, the latter relates both to knowledge-ability and application. Though conceptually easy-seeming to us now, it is not to be supposed that all that was needed was to dash it off in a single draft or sitting. The many admonitions to the practitioner plus several discrete and separate works relating variously to different professional and preprofessional concerns are clear evidence of the real complexity of the subject and the inevitability of a historical evolution within a cultural or subcultural context. It is further remarkable to what extent evolution of a point of view about medicine and those who practice it is marked in the resulting complex definition by *austerity*.

High standards produce the effect of austerity, and austerity leads to high standards in a productive and expanding circle of end-to-end reactions. But high-soundingness marks more the modern that the antique discussions on medicine. The Hippocratic writers seldom seem swept off their feet and are rarely caught rejoicing in the contemplation of their professional navels. Austerity, which is the hallmark of their discussion at its best, is both attractive and seductive; in any case, the goal is close to perfection, however realistically stated, and in the nature of things unsimple to attain.

The Hippocratic writers had several objectives to achieve in those works which they devoted to examining the professional preparation and concerns of the physician. They had first of all to carve out for themselves an area exclusive to their art. Much as they were aided in this by the pre-existing state of the art, its content, and its jurisdiction, there prevailed before they wrote no more than the popular wisdom or foolishness about sickness, health, and the healing done by healers. They had to break away, in this climactic effort of self-definition, both from the temples of the religious and the forums of philosophers. Of the two, both of which were recognized, as the writings in the Collection show, as threats to a rational view of medicine, the temple with its precedence in treatment and therefore in tradition exercised almost unlimited sway in actuality: it was and it functioned, and it rivaled Hippocratic medicine, the collected works of which, insofar as they are polemic, preserve in isolation the shocks of their collision.

The other, the great and lesser philosophers with their disciples and imitators, posed a newer but no less serious threat to the emergence of rational medicine, and they did in fact affect its development negatively, positively, and in a sense permanently. There is indeed a continuing conflict between philosophy, the art or science of speculation, and medicine, the practical art of healing. Though many practitioners may have the mien of philosophy, few have been adept at both. They seem to be and are in some way vocations which are fundamentally antagonistic to each other. Both basically are concerned with man, and both claim, with right, to instruct man. But medicine till now at least has been body-oriented, whereas till now or some future time philosophy has addressed itself to the mind of man and singularly avoided his body. The advent of a psychosomatic medicine in recent times suggests an eventual but yet unsighted resolution of the conflict between the two cultures. The philosopher-physician is as yet as much an un-exampled beast as is the philosopher-king and very likely far more of a desideratum than Plato's ideal has ever been.

So the first great achievement of the rationalist physicians represented in the Collection was to free medicine from religion and from philosophy. Medicine could then exist, grow, and develop apart from both theology (and in its uncritical popular form, superstition) and philosophy. It had, as the author of *Ancient Medicine* said, a principle and method of its own, sufficient to enable it to stand on its own. It may therefore be said that medicine came into being as a rational art when it wrested its territory from encroachment by related and much older human concerns, religion and philosophy. But this should not be considered like a game of opposing sides. Man himself is one and indivisible. All three—religion, philosophy, and medicine—are his concern, and it may be that they are ultimately one concern, but phases and alternations of each other in one same thing. Further, medicine of a prerationalist kind may antedate both religion and philosophy insofar as it dealt with the healing of ungod-ed and unguided bodies.

And so before time was (it hardly is unless recorded) medicine may have been, and it may have had to be, as the author of *Ancient Medicine* supposed, when brutish diets could not serve for man, nor the regime of health suffice for the sick.

The Hippocratic writers had two other major objectives, and there is evidence that they succeeded substantially in achieving them. One was to amass empirically a body of knowledge peculiar to the fledgling profession and somehow to control it and shape it and organize it for the benefit of patient and practitioner. This certainly also involved a running controversy with other schools of medical thought, in particular the Cnidian as opposed to their own, which by all accounts originated and developed first on the island of Cos, the birthplace of Hippocrates. This, then, is a matter of the *content* of medicine, as something separate from the content of either religion or philosophy.

The third objective was to pass all of this on to others. In doing this they created the first cadres and schools and apprenticeships (or internships, if you like) of rationalist medicine.

The seven essays considered in this chapter and the next reveal the ways in which the Hippocratics addressed themselves to attaining these three objectives. It was a great achievement to do so much so well in the time of composition of these essays.

In discussing these essays I have omitted material extraneous to my purpose, which is to delineate the medical practitioner and his profession as the Hippocratics saw them.

The translation of the titles of some of the essays has varied with either the editor or translator. I have altered the translation of two, in one case to have the title reflect the content of the essay, in the other to modernize the English. The seven essays are the following:

(1) *The Oath* (*Horkos*), sometimes—erroneously, as we shall see—called *The Physician's Oath*.

(2) *Medical Education* (the Greek title is *Nomos,* i.e., the physician's *law* or *rule,* but the title I have given it is justified by the subject of the composition).

(3) *The Physician* (*Peri ietrou*).

(4) *Professional Conduct* (*Peri euschemosynes;* the Greek word *euschemosyne* includes the notions of elegance, refinement, decency, respectability, dignified or gentlemanly behavior). Adams uses the title *On Honorable Conduct* for this essay; Jones preferred to use *Decorum,* now rather old-fashioned as a piece of English; Littré and other French scholars generally have used the title *De la Bienséance* (the French word meaning "conformity to social usage"), which comes close enough to the essay's Latin title *De decentia* (*On Propriety*). George Lamb, the translator of H.-I. Marrou's *History of Education in Antiquity,* calls it by the lengthy title, On *the Right Way to Behave,* and German translators have used the title *Ueber den Chic* by borrowing from the French.

(5) *The Clinic* (*Kat' ietreion*).

(6) *Precepts* (*Parangeliai*).

(7) *Aphorisms* (*Aphorismoi*).

The Oath

Of all the writings in the Hippocratic Collection none is more widely familiar than *The Oath.* A survey reported in 1966 indicated that twenty-one of eighty-four medical schools reporting in the United States still administer the Hippocratic Oath to their graduates, or exactly 25 percent of the total number. The ancient oath however was not taken by graduates but by *beginning* students of medicine. To some extent, the Hippocratic and other oaths have been displaced by the Declaration of Geneva, which the World Medical Association adopted in 1948.

Though *The Oath* is widely familiar at present, it can hardly be said that it is widely understood. Scholars and historians of medicine have many questions to raise about its date of composition, its authenticity, terminology, phraseology, and meaning. As for its time of composition, it has been assigned to every century from the sixth century B.C. down into the imperial period of Rome. Ludwig

Edelstein was convinced that it belonged to the fourth century B.C. and that it was a "Pythagorean document" (*The Bulletin of the History of Medicine,* Supplement No. 1, 1943). Whether it is Pythagorean or not I cannot say, but my impression is that it stems from the late fifth or from the first half of the fourth century. *The Oath* is included in the list authored by Erotian in the first century A.D. as a genuine Hippocratic writing, that is, as having been written by Hippocrates of Cos himself, which is improbable. The work is not mentioned by either Bacchius or Celsus, commentators of the second century B.C. and early first century A.D. respectively. In any case, it is a remarkable document, and I have included the entire text of it here in my own translation.

The Oath has four essential parts: the relationship of the oath-taker (1) to his teacher; (2) to his students; (3) to his patients; and (4) a statement of his intended conduct both as a professional person and as a private individual. To make the twelve stipulations of the oath clearer I have avoided the single-paragraph arrangement commonly used and which is a carry-over from the received text in most current translations.

The Oath

(1) I solemnly swear by Apollo the Physician, by Asclepius, Hygeia, and Panacea [All-Heal], and by all the gods and goddesses, whom I call upon to witness this oath, that I shall to the best of my ability and judgment carry out the intent of this oath and this agreement.

(2) I shall consider my teacher in this art as the equal of my parents, I shall share my livelihood with him and even share my substance with him if need be.

(3) I shall consider the male members of his family as my own brothers, and I will teach them this art if they wish to learn it, without payment or written agreement.

(4) I shall impart both written and oral instruction as well as practical instruction to both my own sons and those of my teacher, and to those students who have signed the agreement and sworn to abide by the physician's rule, but to no other person.

(5) I shall use treatment for the good of the sick to the best of my ability and judgment, and I shall refrain from using it for either harm or wrongdoing.

(6) I shall not prescribe a deadly drug (or dose) to anyone even if I am asked to do so, and I shall not suggest or advise the taking of such a drug (or dose).

(7) Likewise, I shall not prescribe for any women the use of a pessary to induce abortion.

(8) I shall conduct my life and the practice of my profession in a pure and holy manner.

(9) I shall not do surgery even on those suffering from (kidney) stones, but I shall yield to practitioners who specialize in this work.

(10) Whatever houses I go into, I shall enter for the good of the sick, avoiding all malicious or destructive wrongdoing, including especially sexual misconduct with persons of either sex, free or slave.

(11) Whatever I see or hear in the course of my ministrations or even beyond the professional sphere of my activities in the society of others, I shall not reveal what ought never to be repeated, as I am convinced that such matters are strictly confidential.

(12) Accordingly, if I carry out the provisions of this solemn oath, and if I do not violate any of them, may it be my reward to enjoy life and the practice of my profession, honored always by all men; but if I transgress any provision or falsely swear to this oath, may I suffer the opposite fate.

Like the Mosaic Code, the *Oath* has ten injunctive provisions. Statements (1) and (12) are purely formal constituents of any solemn oath. The emphasis placed on the debt owed to the teacher is remarkable as well as pleasant, though not unexpected. Statements (3) and (4) serve only to detail the obligation of the trainee to others with the further exclusive provision that instruction is limited otherwise to those under contractual agreement and who have taken the same oath.

The first of the professional clauses of the *Oath* (5) is appropriately general, but the terms in which it is stated are excellent: "to refrain from harm or wrongdoing in the exercise of his profession." Furthermore, treatment is for the good of the sick. Obvious, perhaps, but beyond praise or quibble. No matter how often reiterated, it remains a necessary and welcome statement.

Statements (6) and (7) are particular and negative injunctions against the prescription of poison or pessary. Only doctors have any notion of the frequency with which the means to death or abortion are requested.

Number (8) is another generalized statement: irreproachable conduct, both personal and professional, is the ideal to which the trainee is committed.

Statement (9), with its *apparent* exclusion of surgery as a specialty left to men trained in it, has caused more critical commentary than any other provision of *The Oath*. In the phrase of Friedrich Bœrner it is the *locus maxime vexatus* of the *Oath* (Leipzig, 1751). The reason for this is the conflict of this provision with the evidence of the Hippocratic Collection, which is that surgery of many kinds was practiced. Examples from the Collection are given in Littré's discussion and list (Vol. IV, Argument IV, p. 615–620, *Serment*). Questions raised by this provision have yet to be satisfactorily resolved, as the résumés of both Jones and Ludwig Edelstein show. The most that can be said with surety is that surgery is placed in a very special, restricted category and apparently outside the activity of the medical physician for whom the *Oath* was designed.

Provisions (10) and (11) relate explicitly to moral and ethical conduct: in the one, sexual purity of the physician; in the other, the confidentiality in his safekeeping of *both* patient and non-patient privacy.

It hardly needs to be emphasized how remarkable *The Oath* is as a very early statement definition of medical practice, nor how consistent it is with the ideal image of the practitioner down through the centuries. If there is a "mystique" of the physician, it is first encoded here.

The Oath as a whole breathes the spirit of dedication to the profession and to the sick. It may not now be a perfect or perfectly apposite expression to which all who practice medicine can subscribe. Some of the provisions are archaic or perhaps irrelevant, but a wholly modern statement would not be so much wholly new as a revision based on the essential parts of *Horkos*.

Jones used the term "etiquette" for professional ethics and in this connection makes the following interesting comment: "Medical etiquette was and still is intended to protect the patient and to maintain the dignity of the profession. The latter is perhaps the more important consideration nowadays; in Greek times it was rather the welfare of the patient" (Vol. II, *Introductory Essays* V, p. xxxv).

II   Medical Education (*A Guide for Prospective Practitioners*)

Nomos ("Law" or "Rule") has as its actual subject medical education or the prerequisites for medical practice. Anarchy is the first result of a laissez-faire philosophy among the practitioners of any profession. Next, abuses creep in and begin to swarm. This is the logical point for awareness of abuse to evolve painfully toward self-regulation. In the absence of formal, state-controlled licensure, self-regulation is essential as the minimally adequate means of policing the profession. The problems of malpractice are more serious and complex today than ever. *Nomos* or *Medical Education* reveals the gaps between the ideal and actual practice of medicine. The text that has come down to us is divided into five "chapters" or sections.

In Chapter 1 medicine is characterized as the most distinguished of the professions (*techneon men paseon estin epiphanestate*), but the most disregarded of all of them for two reasons: the ignorance of practitioners and the ignorance of those who judge medicine by such practitioners. The only penalty attached to the practice of medicine is dishonor, which hardly bothers those who are dishonest. The majority are physicians in reputation; very few are physicians in fact.

The modern attitude toward the profession is quite different of course. The doctor's image is quite good. How good it is was measured recently by Louis Harris and Associates. A sample population of two thousand Americans ranked physicians first of seventeen professions and occupations in public esteem and confidence (the doctors scored 74 percent in the survey, compared to 70 percent for bankers, 66 percent for scientists, 65 percent for military leaders, and 62 percent for educators), as reported by *Newsweek* magazine and given wide circulation in the press. No wonder the ancients were concerned with their self-image! It seems that in their day the profession would have scored very low, as low perhaps as the arts and advertising men are said to score now (respectively, with scores of 24 and 22 percent).

The writer of *Medical Education* presupposes for sound training in medicine these requirements: natural aptitude, formal instruction, an appropriate place of instruction, instruction beginning in childhood, diligence, and time (chapter 2). It would be difficult to find a basis for dissent to any of these stipulations in the present.

An agricultural simile is used to illustrate the interrelationship of the requirements: in observing the growth of things in the earth we can see an analogy with medical instruction. Our natural aptitude is like the soil. The teachings of our instructors are like seeds. Learning in childhood resembles the seasonable implantation of the seeds in soil that is prepared to receive them. The place of instruction is like the enveloping air that supplies nutriment to growing things. Diligence corresponds to tilling the soil carefully. Finally, time imparts strength to all of these for their successful ripening (chapter 3). The charm of this analogy is considerable.

These, then, are the preconditions of medical practice. Exact knowledge of medicine must precede peripatetic practice in various towns and cities in order for men to be considered as physicians, not in name alone, but also in fact. Lack of experience is a poor resource to fall back upon: it has no share in confidence or joy but is the nurse of both timidity and recklessness. Timidity indicates inability; recklessness is a sign of lack of skill. Knowledge and opinion are in fact two very different things: the former produces understanding, the latter produces ignorance (chapter 4).

Matters which are sacred are revealed only to men who are holy: the profane have no right to them until they are initiated into the mysteries of knowledge (chapter 5).

This last statement is striking and intriguing. It may support the argument that medical practitioners formed a guild to which entrance was secured by lengthy preparation and an initiation (ceremony), which included the swearing to an oath, from which outsiders (the *bebeloi* or "profane" mentioned above) were strictly excluded. There would be nothing very surprising if ancient physicians looked on themselves as forming an in-group and certainly their many associations and restricted memberships today, and which almost everyone accepts as the norm if not the necessary *modus consociandi,* exhibit this characteristic point of view. The language used is not merely imitative of the language of religious mysteries, it is typical of closed associations with its strong emphasis on the arcane nature of its subject matter and the contrast between the "ins" and "outs"—the holy men and the profane. *Medical Education* is thus another document produced during the classical period of antiquity to which the medical profession owes a portion of its characteristic expression in its historical development. Taken together, the seven essays considered in this chapter are like a Magna Carta of medicine. We begin to see that from the historical point of view medicine has not moved very far from its beginnings, despite the enormous increase in knowledge, in the understanding of the etiology of disease, in the range and depth of chemotherapy, and the availability of research facilities to augment all of these.

What *Medical Education* does not concern itself with is a pro-

gram of courses, the Scylla and Charybdis of most modern attempts
to deal in practical terms with premedical training. I imagine that
if anyone were to ask what the medical student should study and
know, the ancient answer would be something like, "Why, whatever
would help him achieve these goals!" In other words, the really
practical thing is to keep the ends in mind: by so doing we ensure
that the means we choose will subserve the ends we chose.

III   The Physician

That the rationalist school of medicine did admit surgery to its
jurisdiction is evident from most of the writings in the Hippocratic
Collection, in some of which it is the main or sole topic of discussion, as it is in all but the first chapter of *The Physician*. No
ancient source mentions it but it appears to be genuine and Hippocratic.

Here we are concerned only with the author's description of the
physician, and here too we find that the strictures posed by the
author have found their way into the common body of notions
generally entertained by most persons on the subject of the doctor.

There are two sorts of "requirements" which the writer discusses, the external and the internal, or the physical and moral
qualities appropriate to the medical practitioner. The dignity (*pros-
tasie*) of his position requires that he should have a good complexion (*euchros*) and be in good physical condition (*eusarkos*).
We can hardly interpret these two terms to mean "ruddy" and
"fleshy," respectively, as the editors of Liddell-Scott imply. The
reason given by the author makes good popular sense: most people
believe that a person in poor physical condition himself would be
unable to look properly after others. A good, healthy physical
exterior is a kind of advertisement for the efficacy of the doctor's
skill and knowledge: he can "heal himself," *ergo* . . .

Next, he must exhibit cleanliness in his person. His clothing must
be neat and serviceable (*estheti chreste*), and the perfume he uses
pleasant and unobjectionable, without being suspect. All these things
have a good effect on the patient.

The physician must be of good character and give prudent
consideration to his whole style of life, so that his sense of discre-
tion as well as his gentlemanly conduct contribute positively to his
good reputation. He must conduct himself therefore in a gentlemanly fashion toward everyone and display a dignified and affection-

ate attitude toward his fellow man. Since precipitate and hasty behavior is looked down upon, though it has its usefulness, it ought to be avoided. He must be guided by the license permitted him by various circumstances in view of the uniqueness of personal reactions and situations.

Outwardly, he should have the look of one who is thoughtful rather than austere, and he should avoid giving the impression of being self-willed and misanthropic, just as he ought to avoid the other extreme of excessive laughter and gaiety, which is most inappropriate.

His relations with all others must be marked by justice, because justice intervenes in so many relationships and situations.

In general, the contacts of the physician with others who are his patients are important, and as he is constantly dealing with women, and unmarried girls, and very precious objects, he must have good judgment, self-control, and pure conduct.

The author then turns to a description of the doctor's office, its lighting, seating arrangements, instruments, and the availability of water, linen (for bandages), and sponges, and then the use of these, particularly in surgical cases, with comment on the four types of wounds according to their development (fistulous, fungous, serpiginous, and those which result in scar formation, which he calls the only one conformable to nature). Finally, the physician who wants a knowledge of wounds produced by weapons will have to attach himself to some army in the field, most likely a mercenary force, in order to obtain any breadth of familiarity with wounds of this class, which he says are rarely seen in the course of a lifetime within the confines of the cities. That military surgery was an existing branch of medicine at this time is clear from the author's concluding statement in which he refers to his other writings on the subject, which have not come down to us, unfortunately. Littré supposed that it consisted solely of the removal of missiles, but it would surely involve some complexity of treatment.

The evidence is also here for the existence of doctors who maintained an establishment of their own for the treatment of what we would call outpatients, with specialization of facilities, arrangements, and equipment, within the city. Not all were peripatetics, and only a small number attached themselves to the military, in contrast with later Roman imperial practice.

It is interesting that appearance and demeanor are two subjects on which modern medical instruction is largely silent. There is of course a literature of random comment and prescription on the advisability of acting in such a way as to give reassurance to the patient, and samples of the same can be found also in the standard medical textbooks and works of reference. But it is assumed that the home upbringing and the high sense of purpose or dedication which precede the emergence of the young man as a medical student will by and large guarantee the quality of his conduct, while his appearance itself so far as clothing is concerned can be left to the supervision of either his wife or, more likely, "his nurse." Even the modern newspaper medical authority or columnist, who broaches so many topics daily, will speak only of the individual doctor's power of reassurance, but does not discuss it. It is an available item in his armamentarium, but the springs of it are not revealed.

It is also true that motivation for this profession is not so much unique and single but various and manifold. The ancient writer defines in a general way a mean between extremes—some of which he had probably observed from firsthand experience with colleagues. He assuredly is not guilty of the naive error that only one temperament suits the physician. Instead, there is a "norm" with some breadth and elasticity to it, but the extremes are excluded, for reasons which compel general acceptance. And, consistently with expressions which appear elsewhere in the Collection, the two chief reasons are the good of the patient and the good of the practitioner, which in turn redound to the good of the profession as a whole. These considerations—patient, practitioner, and the public image of the profession—are a distinctive feature of the Hippocratic writings as they have come down to us. They subsequently became embedded in medical tradition even if violated by individual practitioners or neglected by some schools of medicine.

Again and again there is expressed the greatest awareness of the sanctity of the doctor-patient relationship, its fragility, and its sensitivity. The physician is constantly dealing with "precious objects" (*tois axiois pleistou ktemasin*). It is not a mistake made by the Hippocratics to take the relationship of doctor and patient for granted, or to assume that it will be the natural concomitant of the study of disease and the life sciences. The banality of virtue makes it difficult to teach and youthful cynicism is a simple cover for confusion. But it appears certain that it, like other attitudes, must be taught and not left to autogenesis, for the majority of practitioners, left to their own devices, are neither philosophic nor humanistic, it must be conceded. The current concern for the humanistic education of doctors is well warranted. Even though many are conscientious and dedicated to very demanding duties, doctors themselves will admit that Oslers are few.

As the acquisition of knowledge increases, its application in the medical area incurs the danger of dehumanization. Automation in medicine, as recently proposed, needs offsetting by genuinely human cybernetics. And, with or without automation, modern medicine could profitably examine in the wellspring of its own beginnings the humanity and humaneness which are characteristic of the Hippocratic Collection. The gaps in knowledge of the ancients were many and enormous, and their theories occasionally absurd, but their judgment *qua* human beings was sound and free of malice and in this area they have a legitimate claim to our respect.

IV   Professional Conduct

For anyone curious about the emergence of the doctor as a professional practitioner, a close reading of *Professional Conduct* (*Peri euschemosynes*) is essential and rewarding, even enjoyable. Both the modern physician and the modern layman will recognize in this essay the earliest and clearest picture of the general practitioner (the "G.P."), his raison d'être, his posture with regard to philosophy and religion, his personal mien and demeanor, his activity as teacher of interns and nurses, his relationship to his patient, his "bedside manner," even to the forerunner of the famous "little black bag," the first-aid contents of which are noted in detail.

Other topics discussed in the essay include the practitioner's aptitude, training (in the two subjects of the apprentice stage), his attitudes, behavior, and relations not only with patients but also with his colleagues, the "paramedical teams," and the public.

The text has been preserved traditionally in eighteen "chapters." As is true generally of early texts of the antique period, a "chapter" is really a paragraph of variable length but seldom over two printed pages long. It owes its existence to a chain of copyists, rarely if ever to the original writer. This charming essay is thus about ten modern pages in length, but its interest and its influence on the medical profession far surpass its modest size.

The first and second chapters are marvelously evocative of the stresses and strains which ended in the disruption of the Athenian state and found its most painful moment in the martyrdom of Socrates (399 B.C.). On the basis of chapter 2 in particular, I would consider it most likely that *Peri euschemosynes* was composed in the first decade of the fourth century. It is dated 350 B.C. by H. Gossen, the author of the article on Hippocrates in Pauly-Wissowa (column 1813). Further, these two chapters may be regarded as reactive either to the peripatetic sophists of the last half of the fifth century or to the Socratics themselves.

Chapters 3–18 are for the most part as free of obvious polemic as of gratuitous austerity; their stamp is that of urbane good humor and a ready, cheerful wit.

The essay is divisible into two main parts. It has a longish but instructive exordium on the relationship of medical practice to philosophy and (much more briefly) to religion. There follows a review of the doctor-patient relationship which is clearly the essence for the writer of the concept of professional conduct. The essay ends with a brief and graceful return to the notions of the exordium, but this time in terms of that precious intangible which has still such compelling power: the good name and fame of the practitioner.

There are, as will appear in the discussion, numerous observations in both divisions of the essay which, when taken together, constitute a code as well as a rationale of medical ethics or professional conduct. As a whole, it forms with *The Oath, Medical Education,* and *The Physician* a compendious but significant testament of the ancient world to which the modern practice of medicine has yet to make a philosophical addition of equal importance.

The ancient Hellenes enjoy still or suffer yet from their enormous reputation for fruitful speculative thought and philosophizing. The greatest of them were dream-ridden and ideal-haunted, and nothing they did or said has contributed more to the renaissance of culture and the flowering of the arts in the modern era than the intensity of their commitment to the dreams and ideals that obsessed them. And yet in all their best achievements and in many lesser ones there is evident to the student their consuming preoccupation with this earth, this race of mankind, this individual, and this living, fleeting moment.

So with the opening chapter of *Professional Conduct* the author expresses a kind of contempt and a rejection of those who do not relate wisdom (*sophie*) to life. This contempt and rejection of impractical speculation recalls the depth of feeling of the Socratics against the physical philosophers both contemporary and precedent whose philosophizing was forever "up in the air" (*ta meteora*).

The writer is firm, even prim, on this subject. For him, most "wisdom" has developed into useless speculation (*pros peri-ergien*)—that is, it is "overdone" to the point of irrelevancy. To the firmness and primness of this is added the wit of a statement to which our saying "the devil makes work for idle hands" surely goes back: "One may put up with this (speculation) just so far that, where idleness is absent, so is mischief: for leisure and in-activity hunt for mischief and are in fact pushed into it, whereas vigilance and reflection are conducive to those things which draw us to the beauty of human existence."[2]

Whatever wisdom's object may be, the truly attractive wisdom (*he chariestere*) is that which has developed into an art, not just any art (or skill) but an art whose application leads to proper professional conduct and a good reputation.

All forms of wisdom which are free of self-seeking and impropriety and which are characterized by an artistic method (*methodos tis eousa technike*) are noble (*kalai*). It may be misleading here to follow Jones in translating *technike* as "scientific," which seems to go far beyond our context.

The author then attacks the "opposition" directly. Shameless traveling purveyors of so-called wisdom succeed in winning popular favor. His next remark is reminiscent of the three ages of man unforgettably described by Aristotle in his *Rhetoric* (Book II, chapters 12–14, 1389a–1390b). Did Aristotle get the inspiration for his exposition from the Hippocratic essayist? The latter says that the young fall easy prey to such hucksters of popular wisdom; that grownups sweat in shame at their sight; and that old people in exasperation (out of irritation or "bitterness," *dia pikrien*) pass legislation to banish them from the state.

This triadic development would neatly fit Aristotle's culminating notion: the young (accept sophistry) because they have in plenty the vitality of young males but lack discipline, the mature (sweat or blush, that is, redden with shame at the recollection of their deception) because they have both the vitality of young males (*and* discipline), and the aged (vent their bitterness on them) because they have the discipline but lack the vitality of young males! But there may be dozens of earlier such triadic passages.

The Hippocratic writer is referring of course to the sophists and his attack on them is based on two fundamental objections: they sell or retail a wisdom which the writer is convinced is false, and then cheapen the art and thus bring all its true practitioners in contempt.

By their externals you shall know them, he warns his young readers: they ply their trade in the market place. Literally, he uses the phrase "they work the agora." This is not the oddity of language Jones construes it to be (Introduction, p. 269) and his translation (p. 281) is simply wrong. The phrase (*agoran*) *ergazomenoi* or its equivalent is attested in writers such as Lysias and Demosthenes. It is further supported by the phrase used of prostitutes, *somati ergazomenai,* for which Liddell-Scott quotes the Latin counterpart, *quaestum corpore facere.* The phrase is either idiomatic with the people who spoke the Greek written in this passage or an imaginative, even brilliant pun; probably it is both, for it is precisely the combination of "profitmaking" and "prostitution" at which the author strikes.

Further, they practice a brand of deception strongly flavored by its vulgarity. (The same word in the Greek, *banausie,* is also used in the sense of "quackery" or "charlatanism" in the essay of Hippocrates on epilepsy, chapter 18, and it may well have this sense here too.) They flit about from one place to another (city or country), their clothing and general appearance are a giveaway.

The last statement in chapter 2 is the strongest of all: in view of their impudent luxury, they are all the more to be avoided and detested by those who observe them.

The asceticism, the moral conviction, the moral indignation, and the high standards relentlessly pursued by the author are not only remarkable in themselves but perfectly suit the demanding sort of dedication ascribed to the best practitioners ever since. It is a fierce and total devotion of the self to a clearly envisioned and firmly grasped ideal.

The remainder of the essay is quite in keeping with this vigorous beginning. It is as if, having once cleared the air of those oppressive thoughts engendered by the observation of huckstering cheats and quacks, he can now breathe forth deep and fresh thoughts on the subject most dear to him, of what a real physician ought to be.

The ideal at which every beginning practitioner should aim is twofold: an external demeanor in keeping with the dignity and the demands of a rigorous profession, and that internal balance of judgment and conviction of which the external accidents are but the reflection. Initially, the author directs his attention to the externals, as instanced elsewhere, but the rest of this middle part of the essay, comprising chapters 3 through 7, is strikingly insightful.

The physician's preparation in matters of dress should be neither overstudied nor overelaborate. Simplicity in apparel is the aim. The advantages of unostentatious clothing are several: such clothing makes a good impression; it fosters sober reflection in the wearer; and it also disposes him to concentrate mentally on his own thoughts as he goes about his business.

The balance of the middle portion of *Professional Conduct* gives an impressive portrait of the ideal physician. Temperament modified by training, malleable nature molded by discipline—this, in brief, is the key to the ideal. Modern taste tends to view ideal formulations with some distrust, and there is good historical warrant for it.

If a way is ever found to date beyond question the composition of *Professional Conduct* and that date proves anterior to the composition of the dialogues of Plato, as now seems possible, if not probable, we shall have fixed upon one or both of two interesting conclusions: either (1) the existence of an ideational climate in which concepts of like nature developed in the same time span in the Ionian Hellas of Asia and Europe, and/or (2) a source of Platonic and subsequent Aristotelian ideation and argumentation. The latter at least is the view expressed in H.-I. Marrou's *History of Education in Antiquity* (Mentor Edition, translated by George Lamb, page 107): "The influence of medicine on Plato's thought was profound, at least equal to that of mathematics . . . and Greek medicine, by a remarkable process of development which can be traced through the fifth and fourth centuries, had come to believe that its fundamental object was not the immediate treatment of sickness but something much wider: the maintenance of health by a proper mode of life. Thus there came to be a close connection between the doctor and the sports-trainer, symbolized in Herodicos of Selymbria, who carried on the two professions at once."

How much that ideal works still in the minds of physicians and controls the actions of the best among them, as it has through the ages, is attested by Dr. Henry E. Sigerist's *The Great Doctors, A Biographical History of Medicine* (translated by Eden and Cedar

Paul, and originally published in 1933 by W. W. Norton, now reprinted in 1958 in paperback form by Doubleday Anchor).

In this connection we can cite as an example of the fascination
of the ideal, the fact that the physician and *littérateur* Francois
Rabelais lectured publicly on the Hippocratic writings in Mont-
pellier and published his edition of the *Aphorisms* in 1532 along
with Galen's *Art of Medicine.*

Traits of Mind and Personality of the Good Physician

These are the traits of mind and personality of the ideal physician,
set forth in a chapter which has a Theophrastean stamp: self-
control; candor; relentless energy in exchanges with others (*pikroi
pros tas synantesias*), that is, the attitude and ability necessary
to give a good accounting of oneself and one's convictions in any
dispute which may arise (presumably, but not necessarily only in
matters of care and treatment); readiness or quickness of thought
which makes for promptness of reply; toughness in the face of
opposition; shrewdness and affability towards one's equals (neither
deceived nor deceiving them); easiness in personal relationships
with all sorts of people; discreet reserve (or perhaps calm per-
severance) in the face of upsetting circumstances; reasonableness
and patient forbearance when confronted with (obdurate) silence;
promptness and readiness to grasp an opportunity when it presents
itself; sensibleness and self-control in eating and drinking; tenacity
in endurance of an opportunity (whether awaited or seized);
ability to express one's teaching in effectively chosen words; a
facility for eloquence; graciousness; ability to support one's own
self in sure reliance upon the solid reputation which results from
these very traits, attitudes, and qualities; and the acceptance of the
self-limitations imposed by the truth of what has been proved,
demonstrated, and taught (chapter 3). Unquestionably, it is a very
tall order.

Natural Ability, or Talent: Nature versus Nurture

The indispensable and controlling factor in making a physician
is, unsurprisingly, natural ability. This makes all the rest possible.
In wisdom, as well as in the art of the medical practitioner, the
essential value, the duty, the office, the service, and the task are
all alike unteachable. It is nature that prepares the way. Subsequent

to the fact of nature it is wisdom that comes eventually to the knowledge of those things already achieved by nature.

There can be no gap between experience, reason, and action. All may be lost if any of these proves defective or wanting. In this chapter (4) the writer reproves those who fail to practice what they preach, as well as those who commit malpractice through ignorance, lack of experience or training, or want of application of reason, and that third group in whom there is a divorce between intellection and action: *to gar oiesthai men, me pressein de, amathies kai atechnies semeion esti,* "for to have ideas and not act upon them is a sign of ignorance and defective professionalism."

Cur medicus (non) deus: Why the doctor is (not) a god.

The ancient Greeks saw *ti theion* (something divine) in every sort of exceptional phenomenon, and especially in the realm of human endeavor and achievement. In Homer, this "divinity" of mere mortals is a commonplace: Achilles, Odysseus, and scores of others are godlike or divine. It is the reiterated theme of Pindar: "only by the grace of God does a man flourish in the wise development of his thought" (*Olympia XI*). Reflexively, Greek thought leads back from divine to human to divine in an unbroken chain. It is so far from blasphemy and most intimately bound up in the Greek lust (no less a word can describe it) for the ideal. I spoke of it above as "haunting dream" and "obsession." It also represents the culmination of a thought process as well as a wish process. The never-ending search, the unwearied traffic in definitions, the constant grappling with realities, typically culminate with the Greeks in the formulation of conclusive, compelling, and enormously attractive ideals. It was this that led Werner Jaeger to subtitle his *Paideia* with the words, *The Ideals of Greek Culture.* Once given their inevitable "final" stamp and form, these ideals pervasively invade the cultures on which they exert their influence and can thereafter never wholly be expunged from the race conscious. Their anteriority, too, ensures their lasting superiority to any subsequent formulation. They are made thus once and for all time, defiant of the flux in the world around us. They have not only this immortality which in itself would be sterile and unadmirable, but the inner power to inspire a following of committed believers. It must therefore correspond, or literally respond to something very deep in human nature. It also calls and is answered. It can be said that men according to their nature seek *to kalon*—the ideal—which hides also under the names of god, excellence, and perfection.

It is only in this context that chapters 5 and 6 of *Professional Conduct* can be understood.

Many a physician has "played god," and many a physician has had a following who worshiped the ground he walked upon. Deity for doctors is dangerous, as indeed it is for all mortals. Men who play god ought first to find out on whose side the game is loaded: it is seldom if ever stacked in favor of the theophant, and it is more likely that the ape of theodicy will turn out, simply, an ape—possibly just a faker. The patient, meanwhile, may be left to muse if he will on the many perils of his vulnerability. Whence waxeth wisdom for him, timely if not too late. Put otherwise, to the extent we deify those who seem able to save us, we cooperate in two evils: the infringement of our own freedom to worship freely and the freedom of him who saves to be himself, good enough for the job to be done, not a god incarnate.

Yet, for the cultural reasons I have suggested above, the author of *Peri euschemosynes* cheerily, eagerly, persuasively, and with almost consummate rhetorical finesse, risks (as we may think) all the capital of his investment in the ideal physician on just such a bold and risky intellectual ploy. The fifth chapter of his work equates all three: true physicianship, true philosophy, true godliness-godlikeness. If we mistrust all such, it may be because we think we see overreaching in it the hard "sell" which engenders its own negative reaction.

But how often must the man of vision and doer have struggled in the aging years of his youth to lay bare and then fast take hold of the in-felt claim to the respect of his contemporaries. They had long since abandoned heroes of war for heroes of statecraft, and them in turn for heroes of wisdom. From his contemporaries he now claims that respect for the heroes of medicine, in whom he sees the real hero-philosopher, god-man, man-god, god-hero, and hero-god. He does not base his argument on the apotheosis of Asklepios.[3]

Out of envy, out of reality, out of understanding, out of insight came the declaration which fixed in literature, as men in fact had historically done with figures like Imhotep and Asklepios, and to a degree with the fully historical Demokedes of Kroton, the long tradition of doctor worship.

Healer, savior, redeemer remain word images of the doctor

worship universally practiced. Its charter of substance is simple human gratitude for the precious "gift of life" and a payment of admiration in tribute to the drama of medical intervention in the face of death and despair.

Primus Graecus homo—the first man to put it in words was an Ionian Greek, the unknown and unidentifiable author of *Peri euschemosynes*: "Translate wisdom into medicine and medicine into wisdom, for the physician is a philosopher, a lover of wisdom who can rival with god (*ietros gar philosophos isotheos*).[4] Nowhere before or since is the doctrine so directly, unashamedly, and trenchantly put. If men must worship men, why not doctors, in whom lies the power of bestowing (and taking) life or ensuring that men shall have it, live it, and enjoy it more abundantly? Nowhere else is the mythos—and the ethos—of the god-doctor more attractively written.

If the human understanding of mere humanly rational thinking beings has yet a further undigested role to play, perform, act out, and reason through, surely here is one eligible for the taking.

The writer sees no important distinction between philosophy and medicine, the latter requires for practice all the qualities inherent in the practice of the former: indifference to money, modesty, a sense of shame, restraint, sound opinion, judgment, peacefulness, steadfastness, cleanliness, the gift of speaking in maxims (*gnomologie*), knowledge of what is good and necessary for life, riddance of impurity, freedom from superstition, and a godlike pre-eminence. Knowledge of the gods is woven into the very mind (of the healer): for medicine enjoys great honor among the gods in all afflictions and accidents (*symptomata*).

The physician ought also to have a good sense of humor (the Greek term used here is *eutrapelia,* "ready wit," not the sort of joking and kidding around which Aristotle defined in the *Rhetoric,* 1398b, as *pepaideumene hybris* or a "cultivated impudence"), since grim austerity is as unwelcome to the well as it is to the unwell.

He has to keep careful watch over himself, not expose his body, nor converse more than necessary with private persons, since this sort of chitchat may bring criticism of his treatment. He is at pains to avoid overdoing things as well as ostentation (*phantasie*). Training in these matters will obviate their lack when the need for them arises (chapter 7).

Readiness is everything: this applies to any number of things which prior practice can simplify for the practitioner: palpation, anointing, and washing, for the skillful movement of the hands, when lint, compresses, bandages, the products of recovery, and drugs, for wounds and eye disorders, are involved. The idea is to keep in readiness whatever may need to be used, including instruments, appliances, knives, and all the rest. Lack of these will cause helplessness and damage.

The physician must have a second, smaller, handbag suitable for traveling about, and it ought to be one in which the contents are carefully chosen and arranged. The physician's handbag should contain the following: various drugs with whose properties the physician is perfectly familiar; emollients of different kinds according to their use; strong potions prepared by kinds according to prescription; purgatives of all sorts for various needs; and, presumably, the equipment in part at least mentioned just above (chapters 9–10).

It is a good idea to have some advance notion both about what one can expect to find when he answers a call and how one plans to deal with it. If one is fully prepared, he will be able to go directly to work and be helpful, since many cases require immediate action and there is not time for involved reasoning.

Further instructions to the visiting physician include the following: attention on entering the patient's room to his posture when he sits down, maintaining a reserve, with attention to his clothing's arrangement (more necessary then than now in view of the difference in dress), authoritative manner, brevity in speech, self-composure, good bedside manner, concern for the patient, firm response to objections, calm stability in the face of any disturbances which occur, appropriate rebuke of confusion and clamor, and readiness to perfrom his services (chapter 12).

The physician must make frequent calls on the same patient in order to observe carefully all phases in the progress of the ailment and its treatment, since changes in condition supervene quickly, and the patient's welfare requires close periodic checking. This also has the advantages of putting the attending physician at ease and gives him fuller confidence from his familiarity with the stages in the course of treatment (chapter 13).

Patients have their faults and often lie about their taking the prescribed treatments in the doctor's absence. They tend not to admit what they did, and in the event of their death the blame for the consequences of their failure to follow orders falls upon their physicians (chapter 14).

Ministering to the patient should be done in a calm and dexterous way, and most of what the doctor does should be concealed from the patient; the doctor should encourage the patient to accept necessary treatment and by his own cheerful calm divert the patient's anxious attention to himself; the patient may require sharp reproof or solicitous attention and comforting, without however disclosing to him his present or future condition, since in many instances patients in more or less serious condition have worsened from such information (chapter 16).

The instructions given in chapter 17 are of especial interest for the evidence they give of medical attendants responsible to the physician in charge. It is clear from the language used that these are medical students if not male nurses, and the context shows the latter to be quite probable since continuous bedside care is precisely what is enjoined on these initiates in the art. In a sense which is quite real and not metaphorical, nursing is the skill that precedes full responsibility for patient care.

These instructions are clear and unambiguous. One of the students is to be in charge during the doctor's absence to see that his instructions are carried out (without harshness) and care for the patient as ordered. The person chosen must already be initiated in the subject matter of the art, to add what is needed or to assist safely.

The person in charge is placed on duty to forestall loss of information in the intervals between visits by the attending physician. In no case should laymen be entrusted with such matters, since if anything goes wrong the blame will fall upon the physician.

Clarity of plans for treatment is essential for communication to the charge person and the success of treatment; again, the reputation of the physician is at stake, and blame may be subsequently avoided by telling the person in charge in advance whatever needs to be done.

All the matters discussed in the foregoing contribute to the physician's good reputation and dignity, just as they do in wisdom as well as medicine, and generally in all the other arts.

The standards of practice enjoined by *Professional Conduct* are remarkable not only because of their high level, but also because they are practical and valid. The variation from views we now subscribe to is notably small, even negligible. It is a classic statement of the physician, the role he must play, and the three views of him which have done most to shape his conduct: the view of the patient, of the public, and his own view of himself.

CHAPTER 4

The Practice of Medicine

I The Clinic

The Clinic (*Kat' ietreion*) is oriented specifically to the surgeon and in particular to the orthopedic surgeon. The subject matter is *cheirourgie* ("surgery" or orthopedics), and the practitioner is usually referred to as the "surgeon" or "operator" (*ho cheirizon, ho dron*). The chief topics of the essay are, broadly, the operating room and its facilities and the activities performed there, mainly reduction of fractures and splinting and bandaging, with very detailed exposition of the latter. There is no suggestion whatever that orthopedics is excluded from the purview of the general medical practitioner. Though wounds are referred to (by the term *sinos,* or some participial periphrasis), incision is not mentioned, and the method of treatment is by application of bandages (for immobilization of the affected part, reduction of fracture, topical pressure) and, less often, splints (*narthekes*).

Our chief concern with this essay is in the picture it gives of the practitioner. The operator is attended by several assistants (*hyperetai*), who may be medical students, male nurses, or orderlies. The facilities are specialized for the purposes of the activities to be performed. Instruments (*organa*) and orthopedic apparatus (*armena*) are required. They are not described, though splinting and especially bandaging are fully discussed.

The operator is responsible for modifying the light available according to his particular needs, with consideration for the procedure to be used, the comfort and modesty of the patient, and the convenience of the examiner. Artificial light may be required to improve the view of the part or parts to be examined but this should not be done in such a way as to embarrass the patient.

There is a detailed description of various positions to be assumed by the medical examiner and by the patient: convenience, comfort, and suitability for the procedure to be performed are the criteria for preferring one posture to another.

The operator is required to have fingernails of the right length: not too long and not too short. He should have good hands, the "hands of a surgeon," and he should practice frequently all the various procedures common to the clinic. The object of all this is to attain a high degree of ability, adroitness, quickness, effortlessness, dexterity, and skillfulness.

The orthopedic understanding of the writer seems, at least to a layman, to be quite good, and there is a reassuring note in the writer's constant concern for appropriate treatment and the comfort of the patient undergoing treatment. The emphasis is always on quickness of performance when this will reduce pain and on the adequacy of the treatment to secure the desired improvement.

II   Precepts

Precepts (Parangeliai) is a loosely connected series of comments on various aspects of medical practice, some thoretical, some philosophical, but most of them pragmatic or practical. We might re-title it *Advice to the Medical Practitioner,* and this, though longer than the traditional title which I have retained, would be more meaningful to the reader than the uncommon term, "precepts." The essay, not a long one, was quoted by Erotian but not listed by him. Its manuscript tradition is also a troublesome one, and this suggests that numerous inaccuracies may have crept into the text in the various recopyings which it underwent. It is also the source of one of the most admired statements in the entire Collection. W. H. S. Jones was the first to translate the work into English (for the Loeb edition).   Since the work has no single consecutive pattern, plan, or development of thesis, it seems best to select here those topics which bear most directly on the subject matter of this chapter.

Theory and Practice

Sense perception is the source from which we draw both knowledge and experience. It is the intellect which by its faculty of working rationally converts the raw data of experience into knowledge, with conclusions firmly based on observable phenomena. It must be understood that human nature is moved and taught by the vast variety of the world about it, as by the effect of some underlying force. As reason begins to deal with these impressions, it leads us to the truth. But words are not enough in themselves to create truth; by themselves and unsupported by evidential facts, they create only "word-facts," a treacherous and deceptive ground on which to base one's practice. So in one's generalizations the facts must be firmly and consistently followed if one is going to have the ready and unerring habit to which we give the name of "medical practice." Even laymen may be a fruitful source of information with good results for treatment,and the practitioner ought not to hesitate to seek such information (chapters 1–2).

Fees for Professional Services Rendered

There should not be undue concern over fees on either the patient's side or the doctor's side. Setting a fee should be secondary of course to caring for and reassuring the patient. The doctor should not be overly anxious about his fee and ought to postpone even discussing it. If one does mention a fee at the outset, the tendency is for the patient to feel that he will be abandoned without treatment if there is no agreement on the fee. Anxiety, expecially in the acutely ill patient, is harmful for him, and the doctor should avoid causing or contributing to such anxiety. The course of the illness may be very rapid, and promptness of care is essential, so the good doctor seeks not so much profit as the enhancement of his reputation. It is much better and more effective for the purpose to shame a patient whom your efforts have saved into payment, than to squeeze your fee out of those who are actually dying. Patients may face the demands of their illness with ignorance, which should be corrected rather than punished: if a man has honestly subscribed to the requirements of the medical profession, he will practice his art with compassion, always seeking the good of his patient and a way to help him and restore him to good health, which is the real reward of the physician, not to mention his readiness and eagerness to learn (chapters 4–5).

The writer then urges kindness on the physician and consideration of the patient's economic means. Occasionally, the doctor should give his services without charge (*proika*) either in return for a previous favor or for the good of one's current reputation. Should the opportunity present itself of helping a stranger who has no financial resources, such persons should always be fully assisted, *for where there is love of one's fellow man, there is also love of the art of medicine* (*en gar pare philanthropie, paresti kai philotechnie*). The humanity of this statement cannot be questioned or improved upon.

His next statement is also indicative of deep understanding. Though some patients confront the seriousness of their condition with full awareness, they recover largely because they rely with justifiable confidence on the compassionate concern of their physician. He has a threefold task: to care for the ill to make them well, to look after the well to keep them well, and to look after himself for professional reasons (*heneken euschemosynes*) (chapter 6).

"Quacktitioners"

The quack doctor is dependent on luck, the wealthy, and the ignorant, and most often all three in combination. The quack avoids serious or terminal cases and also avoids consultation with other physicians in his mistrust of outside help. He preys on patients whose recovery is prevented by the lack of competent care. Such patients exhaust themselves and their financial resources in a vain search for informed treatment (chapter 7).

Consultation with Other Physicians

It is no breach of professional conduct to consult with other physicians when the doctor in charge is either inexperienced or baffled by the patient's failure to respond to treatment; on the contrary, it is all to the good to have co-workers when much help is needed, and the doctor should urge his patient to permit such consultation. Physicians called upon for consultation ought to conduct themselves professionally: they must avoid jealousy, quarreling, and faultfinding with each other, since those who do this show that they really belong in the marketplace, not in the medical profession (chapter 8).

Reassurance: Its Beneficial Effect on Patients

The doctor ought by all means to relieve the patient of as much anxiety as possible. A patient under care of a good practitioner will be more cooperative and hopeful of full recovery as well as better able to bear the strains of illness and his impatience to be well again. Lacking care, the sick often abandon hope, give in to their illness, and so die. But the physician has it in his power to help the patient combat his disease, to promote his healing, to rally his resources, to help nature do its curative work, and by doing these things remove this patient's anxiety, mistrust, and depression. The goal is restoration to health and this is defined as a natural state, having its own natural motion, not foreign but fitting, and achieved through breathing, warmth, the interaction of fluids, and thorough-

going regime, assuming no congenital or postnatal defect, and even
in such a case to bring the patient's condition as far as possible to
the norm (chapter 9).

The Physician's Dress

Expensive or elaborate headgear and fancy perfume should be
avoided. The point is that excessive or ostentatious dress gives
rise to criticism and the physician's reputation is injured thereby.
On the other hand, the author expressly avoids censure of the
desire to please, which he feels is well within the dignity of the
professional practitioner (chapter 10).

Public Lectures

The writer has little use for physicians who like to lecture to lay
audiences: the ambition is unworthy in itself, and the temptation
to quote poetry is especially bad. His reason for the latter remark
is that by quoting poetry the doctor shows inability and lack of
application, since poetry is irrelevant to medicine and brings to
medicine a grace of its own rather than one germane to medicine,
in other words empty elegance rather than applicable content
(chapter 12). The fault may seem more amiable to us in a day and
age when very few doctors are guilty, when lecturing to laymen
(even commoner now than then), of quoting poetry.

Late-learning

Opsimathie is the Greek for "late-learning." Apparently, as a
fault it was common enough to warrant censure, for the author
of *Precepts* devotes chapter 13 to attacking it and the faults that
accompany it. The late-learner has little experience to fall back
upon, and he can only recall what he sees in front of him. This
leads in turn to all sorts of unseemly and unprofessional behavior,
including frantic oaths, flowery language calculated to dazzle the
layman, and poor observation of facts or recognition of the phenomena observed, with inadequate definitions of disease conditions.
The consultation of such late-learners should be scrupulously
avoided, since the desired goal is confidence and skill in practice
rather than hairsplitting and subtle difference in opinion, which are
better heard than practiced.

The concluding chapter of *Precepts* (14) is composed of a group
of largely unrelated ideas. One of these is the gnomically stated
proposition that "Youth, the prime of life, has all the charming

things about it, whereas the decline, Old Age, has only the opposite."

It is also in this chapter that we find the shortest and simplest definition of *krisis* or "crisis": it is the process of getting rid of disease (*apolysis nousou*).

There is an interesting sentence in this chapter which ascribes one type of incoherence in speech to those who are "in love with their art" (*philotechnousin*): in the wealth of their thinking, their thoughts outstrip their rapidity of speech and so they stumble over their words. It is a good description of a variety of "pressure of speech."

III Aphorisms

The Greek word *aphorismoi* which serves as the title of the essay discussed in this chapter is defined as meaning "pithy sentences," but the term also bears in its matrix the now accessory but originally primary notions of "definitions," "distinctions," and "delimitations." The *Aphorisms* attributed to Hippocrates himself (in modern times by Littré and Jones, among others) exhibit the characteristics of all these meanings severally and together. The work has come down in seven sections, each with a primary subject or group of subjects fairly closely connected for the most part. Excluding some doublets (or pairs with the same numbers), there are in seven sections 412 statements or aphorisms. In addition, an unnumbered group of "pseudo-aphorisms" early became attached to the last of the seven *tmemata* or sections. Though only the very first aphorism in the collection forms a general statement about the practice of medicine (and it may be the most familiar expression in all the Hippocratic corpus), the work itself is included here for the reason that it is an exemplary embodiment of Hippocratic medicine. Obviously, we shall have to approach it in a different way in order to extract from it its general frame of applicability to the medical practitioner and his profession, and the statements which specifically relate to this or that disease entity must be reconsidered from the point of view of the practitioner to whom the *Aphorisms* was addressed.

First Section (*Tmema Proteon*)

The most famous phrase in the Hippocratic Collection comes from the very first of the *Aphorisms*. It is so often misquoted or quoted out of context that we need an effort to restore it to its original context. "Life is short, Art long" is either meaningless or means anything you want it to mean. The full aphorism reads thus: "Life is short, whereas the demands of the (medical) profession are unending, the crisis is urgent, experiment dangerous, and decision difficult. But the physician must not only do what is necessary, he must also get the patient, the attendants, and the external factors to work together to the same end." No other aphorism in the seven sections approaches this one in generality. The others form, in fact, a kind of brief manual of medicine, stating in the most condensed way a clinical picture, a prognosis, a recommended or disapproved therapy. The point of the aphorism here translated is not that there is some (unspecified) contrast between life and art, but a conflict between the shortness of time at one's disposal and the endless demands of one's craft, which involve urgency, experimentation or trial, and decision-making (respectively, in Greek, *kairos, peira,* and *krisis*). What the author is talking about is not some "mystique" of art, as the usual (truncated) quotation implies, but the extraordinary pressures which the professional man must contend with in the practice of medicine. That this is so is clear from the second half of the aphorism: the context is exclusively medical.

The *First Section* is chiefly concerned with "regimen" or dietary restrictions and their effects. The generality of the pronouncement made is evident in these typical statements:

(4) Restricted or strict diets are dangerous; extremes must be avoided.

(5) On a restricted diet the patients make mistakes and therefore suffer worse harm, since any slight deviation is more serious. The same applies to healthy persons who are placed on very strict diets.

(9) Diets must be adapted to individual needs and not exceed individual strength or capacity.

(10) If the ailment "peaks" at once, the diet must be restricted immediately.

(13) Ability to fast is contingent on patient age: old people tolerate fasting most easily, mature adults less easily, young people poorly, and children very poorly, especially if they are very active [hyperkinetic].

(14) Growing bodies have the most inborn heat, so they require the most food, without which they are bound to waste away. Old people have little heat in them and so need less "fuel," in fact too much "fuel" puts out the fire. Their fevers are less apt to be highly elevated because their bodies are cold.

(15) The alimentary tract is naturally hottest in winter and spring, and these are the seasons when sleep is longest, so diets must be increased at these times.

(16) Liquid diets are good for those who have fever, particularly for children and those habituated to such a diet.

(18) Food is hardest to digest in summer and fall, but is most easily digested in winter, less so in spring.

(20) During or immediately following a crisis in the course of an ailment, the patient should be left alone: avoid changes (or novelties) in therapy, as well as drugs (cathartics and emetics in particular) and other irritants.

Second Section

The collection of aphorisms in the Second Section is much more diverse in subject matter than that of the *First Section,* though there is occasionally evidence of a "stringing together" of statements on the same topic recurrently. There is also the good possibility that the collector of these aphoristic statements had in mind as his working context or frame of reference the response of the human organism to various states of ill-health and treatment. In any case, as with the other *Sections* discussed below, each is a loosely organized compendium of therapy.

The first three aphorisms in the *Second Section* are about sleep:

(1) If sleep causes pain, the ailment is very serious.
(2) If delirium terminates in sleep, this is good.
(3) Excess of sleep or insomnia is bad.

The next several are topically random:

(4) Any unnatural excess is harmful.
(5) Tiredness without apparent cause is a sign of some diseases process.
(6) Insensitivity to pain indicates perceptual awareness (gnome) is affected.

There is no need to include all the aphorisms here, nor would there be room to do so. Instead, I have selected some of those which appear most interesting:

(16) Bed rest or restricted activity is essential for those patients who are deprived of food or fasting.

(17) Nourishment beyond that tolerated by the patient's condition, merely complicates recovery.

(21) Inebriation removes hunger (for solid foods).

(22) Diseases caused by excess or defect are healed by their opposites.

Aphorisms 23–32 relate to various stages or developments in the progress of the patient or his disease:

(23) Acute illnesses reach crisis in fourteen days.

(24) The fourth day of illness is a clue to the seven days; the eighth is the beginning of a second seven; the eleventh must be observed carefully since it is the fourth day of the second seven; likewise the seventeenth.

(25) Quartan fever in summer is usually short, whereas in fall it is lengthy, and even more so if near to winter.

(26) Convulsion followed by fever is better than fever followed by convulsion.

(30) Symptoms are weakest at the beginning and the end, and strongest at the peak.

(31) A good appetite which does not improve the condition of a convalescent patient indicates trouble.

(32) Patients whose appetite is initially good but do not improve finally lose their appetite; the reverse is better.

Aphorisms 35–37 are on the use of cathartics (purgatives):

(35) Thinness and wasting are contraindications to the use of cathartics.

(36) Healthy individuals are soon weakened by the use of cathartics; the same applies to those on a poor diet.

(37) Persons in good health are hard to purge.

Numbers 39–40 concern elderly men:

(39) Old men for the most part are sick less than young ones, but their illnesses, if chronic, usually persist till death.

(40) Sore throat and coryza (cold) in the very aged do not exhibit the phenomena associated with *pepsis* [apparently, the changes normally occurring in the younger population].

Aphorism 43 seems out of place:

(43) Those who are hanged [or strangled] and then released, without as yet having deceased, do not regain consciousness if there is foam around the mouth.

As is the case with so many of the aphorisms, number 44 has a modern medical sound:

(44) People who are excessively overweight (by nature) are far more apt to die suddenly than those of average weight.

Aphorism 45 is one of the large number of remarks in the Collection as whole which relate to epilepsy:

(45) Changes, particularly in age, climate, locality, and living habits, affect a cure in young epileptics.

(47) The formation of pus causes more pain and fever than after formation is complete.

(48) In every movement of the body which produces pain, immediate rest relieves discomfort.

(49) Persons in the habit of regular activity and exertion, even if they are frail or elderly, endure more easily than strong and young people who are unused to such activity.

(51) Excess and rapid changes are dangerous, either in emptying, filling, heating, or cooling the body; indeed every excess is inimical to nature, whereas gradual change is safe, especially from one state to another.

(54) A large tall frame is generous and not unpleasing in young people, but in the elderly it is less useful and they are worse off than those who are smaller.

Third Section

The *Third Section* (*Tmema Triton*) begins with the topic of seasonal changes to which are ascribed numerous diseases, which are discussed briefly—perhaps it would be more accurate to say "listed"—in Aphorisms 5–23, and the *Section* concludes with a group of eight Aphorisms (24–31) which relate various diseases to the age of the patient.

Aphorisms 1–4 give a kind of general framework to the particularistic observations which follow. We are told that it is primarily the changes in seasons which occasion disease and within seasons the fluctuations of cold or warmth (1). Some patients show greater sensitivity to summer conditions, others to those of winter, indicating a range of inherent adaptability to one climate or another (2). Conversely, it may be said that some diseases and some ages are variously adapted to seasons, regions, and diets (3). Diseases typical of autumn are to be expected when, in any season, cold and heat occur on a single day (4).

A prevailing south wind (*notoi*) will cause dullness in hearing, dimness of vision, heaviness in the head, sluggishness, and relaxation: typically, these are characteristics of the winds themselves (5). Conversely, a north wind (*boreion*) will cause coughing, soreness in the throat, hard stools, painful urination with shivering, and pains in the sides and in the chest.

A disease can occur at any time of the year, but its severity and the likelihood of its occurring in one season rather than another is dependent on the characteristics of that season (19). Further, seasons which develop according to the norm expected of them, are likely to have diseases of less severity, more typical development, and simple or easy crises (8). The worst season is autumn, for severity of disease and for fatal outcome; in both respects, spring is the best season (9).

A tabular index of the most prominently mentioned seasonal diseases would look like this (numbers in parentheses refer to the Aphorisms):

Autumn	Winter	Spring	Summer
Consumption (10)	Pleurisy,	Melancholia,	Persistent fevers,
Summer diseases,	Pneumonia,	Madness,	Burning fevers,
Quartans,	Lethargic fevers,	Epilepsy,	Tertian fevers,
Intermittent fevers,	Colds,	Hemorrhages,	Vomiting,
Spleen ailments,	Hoarseness,	Laryngitis,	Diarrhea,
Dropsy,	Coughs,	Colds,	Ophthalmias,
Strangury,	Pains in side, chest & loins,	Hoarseness,	Earaches,
Lientery,	Headaches,	Coughs,	Mouth ulcers,
Dysentery,	Dizziness,	Leprosy,	Genital rot,
Sciatica,	Apoplexy (23)	Skin eruptions,	Sweating (21)
Laryngitis,		Growths,	
Asthma,		Arthritic complaints (20)	
Ileus,			
Epilepsy,			
Madness			
Melancholia (22)			

Rainy weather generally leads to high fevers, loose stools, rots, epilepsy, apoplexy, and laryngitis.

Dry weather, on the other hand, produces consumption, ophthalmias, arthritic complaints, strangury, and dysentery (16).

A northerly constitution during the day has a bracing effect: the complexion is improved and so is the sense of hearing, but the effect on the bowels, eyes, and any preexisting upper respiratory complaint may be adverse. A southerly constitution will have a contrary effect: there is a relaxation and moistening of the body which in turn produce heaviness of the head, dullness of hearing, dizziness, painful movement of eyes and the body generally, as well as watery stools (17).

Young people enjoy good health most of all in spring and early summer; old people, in summer and early autumn; the middle-aged, in late autumn and winter (18).

A southerly winter, followed by a northerly spring, may cause abortion in women due to give birth in spring; if the fetus is carried to term, the offspring is apt to be sickly, may die at once or grow up weak and prone to poor health, if it survives (12).

The last eight aphorisms on the *Third Section* (24–31) identify the diseases typical of succeeding age groups. In the newborn and very young one encounters thrush (*candida albicans,* an infection of the oral tissues), vomiting, coughing, wakefulness, fears, inflammation of the navel, and fluid in the ears (24).

The onset of dentition may be accompanied by gum irritations, fever, convulsions, diarrhea, particularly when the canines erupt, and when children are excessively overweight or normally constipated (25).

Older children are susceptible to tonsillitis, displacement of the cervical vertebra just below the inion (or occipital bone), asthma, stone, round worms, ascarides (apparently, a variant of "round worms"), thin-necked warts, swelling of the glands near the ears (but the word may be descriptive of satyr-like swellings of the temples: *satyriasmoi*), scrofulous swelling of the neck glands, and various growths (tumors, neoplasms, tubercles).

The next older group of children retain the same ailment susceptibility as above as they progress to puberty as well as from fever of longer duration and nosebleeds (26–27).

In young males (*neeniskoi* is a term of somewhat vague application but in the line of Pythagoras quoted in Book VIII of Diogenes Laertius it includes the second twenty years of life), among other diseases, mentioned above, there is incidence of bloodspitting, phthisis, acute fever, and epilepsy (29).

Those in the range of forty to sixty years of age are susceptible to asthma, pleurisy, lung inflammation, sluggishness, inflammation of the brain (*phrenitis*), acute fever, persistent diarrhea, cholera, dysentery, lientery (incomplete digestion, or perhaps failure of digestion), and hemorrhoids(30).

The complaints of old age are numerous and familiar: dyspnoea (painful or difficult breathing), nasal catarrh and coughing, strangury, dysuria, joint pains, nephritis, dizzy spells, apoplexy ("stroke"), debility, generalized itching, insomnia, accumulation of fluid or discharge in bowels, eyes, and nose, amblyopia (dimness of vision), glaucoma, and loss of hearing (31).

Fourth Section

Topics discussed in the *Fourth Section* of *Aphorisms* are of less general interest and too particularized to permit of detailed mention here beyond this indication of their content: instructions for purging patients under various conditions and in a variety of ailments occupy Aphorisms 1–20; 21–28 describe various stools and their significance; 29–71 are interpretative of fevers, sweats, and crises; and 72–83 chiefly describe urine in various disease states and its significance in each. The range of comment and observation is impressive.

Fifth Section

The content of the *Fifth Section* is somewhat diverse. The *Section* begins with fifteen aphorisms in most of which the symptoms adduced in various ailments are regarded as prognostic of death. Excluding Aphorism 6, the first seven indicate the probable consequence of *spasmos* or convulsions which may develop in the course of a variety of ailments. Number 6 states that tetanus (defined as "convulsive tension") will result in death in four days or else the patient, having passed the fourth day, will survive.

Aphorisms 16–25 are concerned with the effects of heat and cold on the organism, and primarily as harmful or helpful in different ailments, or in different parts of the body.

But the largest number of aphorisms in the *Fifth Section* is gynecological in subject matter (numbers 28—62). Among the topics discussed are the following: bathing during menstruation (aromatic steam baths are recommended), purgation during pregnancy between the fourth and seventh months; miscarriage; vomiting of blood (a cure for it is menstruation); nosebleed (a good sign if the menses are suppressed), hysteria; painful labor (both helped by sneezing!); conditions of the breasts during pregnancy, complexion in gravid women (a good complexion indicates the child will be male, conversely, a bad complexion indicates the child will be female), weight and nutrition in pregnancy, expulsion of the afterbirth (induced by sneezing and interrupting the intake of air through nose and mouth); significance of various states of the uterine cervix and os; barrenness (the diagnostic test for this condition is to fumigate the patient and then decide whether the smell of the perfume used has penetrated the body as far as the mouth and nostrils); a diagnostic test for pregnancy using hydromel (a mixture of honey and water) before the patient retires for the night: if colic ensues, the patient is pregnant, otherwise not; menstruation during pregnancy (apparently considered both possible and dangerous to the embryo); amenorrhea accompanied by nausea indicates pregnancy; the uterus in women who do not conceive is dense and cold, or watery, or excessively dry.

The remaining aphorisms in the *Fifth Section* (63–72) cannot be readily interrelated, as indicated by their topics: male fertility, effects of giving milk in various ailments, wounds and swellings on them, pains at the back of the head (relieved by cutting the straight vein in the forehead), shivering in women and men (originates in the back and passes to the head), quartan fever and convulsions, condition of the skin and its significance when dry and tight, or loose and sweaty, and lastly, the relative absence of flatulence in cases of jaundice (72).

Sixth Section

There is considerable variety in subject matter among the aphorisms in this section also. If there is one way to characterize these statements as a group, it may be to say that most of the sixty aphorisms refer to symptoms which develop in the course of a disease and whether or not such and such a symptom is benign. I have selected here two classes of statements: (1) those which have a related subject matter, and (2) individual statements of particular interest.

OBSERVATIONS ON GOUT.   The Greek word for gout is podagra. The author has these comments to make about it:

(28) Eunuchs do not contract gout and they do not become bald.
(29) Gout does not occur in females unless the menses are suppressed.
(30) Gout does not occur in young males prior to sexual intercourse.
(49) Inflammation in cases of gout subsides in forty days.
(55) Gouty attacks flare up in spring and fall.

OBSERVATIONS ON MELANCHOLIA.

(11) Hemorrhoids in sufferers of melancholy and kidney inflammation are a good sign.

(23) If fear or despair persists for a long time, this is indicative of melancholy.

(56) In cases of melancholy, the localization of the melancholic humor may have these dangerous consequences: generalized stroke, convulsions, mania [i.e., "madness"], or blindness.

Number (21), however, tells us that madness is removed by supervening varicosities or hemorrhoids.

OBSERVATIONS ON DIARRHOEA.

(15) Spontaneous vomiting removes chronic diarrhea.

(16) Diarrhea which develops in cases of pleurisy or pneumonia is a bad sign.

(17) Diarrhea in a patient suffering from ophthalmia is a good sign.

(32) Stutterers are especially susceptible to persistent diarrhea.

SOME UNRELATED OBSERVATIONS.

(4) Ulcers are malignant if there is loss by scaling of the surrounding epidermis.

(10) In headaches accompanied by severe pain, loss of fluid (pus, water, or blood) by way of the nostrils, ears, or mouth, terminates the ailment.

(18) A severe wound in any of the following is fatal: bladder, brain, heart, diaphragm, small intestine, stomach [perhaps chest or gut is meant here, since *koilie* refers to any of these], or liver.

(24) A segment of the small intestine does not unite if severed.

(38) It is better not to treat cases of hidden cancer: for those who are treated die quickly, whereas the untreated survive for a considerable period of time [possibly a reference to metastasis following treatment].

(50) Fever and vomiting of bile invariably follow any puncture of the brain.

(51) Persons in good health who suddenly suffer from pains in the head, losing the power of speech, and breathe stertorously, die in seven days unless fever supervenes.

(53) Delirium accompanied by laughing is safer than when accompanied by seriousness.

(54) Breathing broken by sobbing is a bad sign in acute infections accompanied by fever.

(57) Strokes (cardiovascular accidents) occur mostly between the ages of forty and sixty.

Seventh Section

This part of *Aphorisms* contains the largest number of observations, eight-seven in all. Although an attempt has been made by the compiler of this *Section* to bring together aphorisms which have a common subject, most of the aphorisms are sequentially unrelated and quite diverse. Related observations are found in aphorisms 31–36 (urine), 63–66 (fevers), 70, 73–74 (unremitting fevers), 67–69 (evacuations and discharges), 79–81 (vomiting, purgation of pus, cephalic flux, diarrhea, and bladder discharges).

But perhaps the most interesting are the unrelated observations, of which a few may be quoted here:

(1) A chill of the extremities in acute diseases is a bad sign.

(5) If madness is followed by dysentery, dropsy, or disorientation (the Greek word here is *ekstasis*), each is a good sign.

(7) Rigidity and delirium after excessive drinking [polyposie] are bad signs.

(9) Delirium or convulsions following hemorrhage are bad signs.

(12) Phrenitis following pneumonia is a bad sign.

(14) Concussion may result in stupor or delirium and either one is a bad sign.

(18) Convulsions or delirium supervening on insomnia are bad signs.

(25) Purgation may precede fatal convulsions.

(40) Sudden paralysis of the tongue or a localized "stroke" may indicate melancholia.

(58) Whatever the cause of a brain concussion, immediate loss of speech is the necessary result.

(72) Excess of sleep or sleeplessness is a disease.

(82) Few recover from phrenitis if they are over forty years of age

(whereas they run less risk where the disease is related both to the constitution and the age of life).

(83) A voluntary flow of tears in illness is a good sign, an involuntary flow, conversely, is a bad sign.

But the most striking of all the observations in this *Section* is the very last:

(87) Diseases which are not susceptible to treatment by the use of drugs are treated surgically; if not susceptible to surgical treatment, they are treated by the use of fire; if not susceptible to treatment by fire, it is necessary to consider them as incurable [or, not susceptible to any form of treatment].[1]

CHAPTER 5

Therapeutics—The Management of Disease

There is no demonstrable beginning of treatment which is properly a beginning of medicine generally, nor is there a second point, nor a middle, nor an end; rather, we begin treatment sometimes by speaking, sometimes by acting, and finish in the same way; and in speaking, we do not begin from the same statements, not even if we are speaking of the same objects, nor do we end with the same statements; and likewise, in acting, we neither begin treatment nor end it with the same actions.

—*Diseases,* Book I, Chapter 9.

I *Case Histories* (Epidemics, *Books I and III*)

Theory and practice necessarily differ. They also tend to complement and reflect one another; even as the former may be invented to account for the latter, so the latter may be modified as the former becomes better understood, or clearer, or truer. Although this chapter deals with therapeutics, which is the management or treatment of diseases, I shall begin with a discussion of the forty-two case histories which have come down to us, even though there is minimal reference in them to actual treatment. In these case histories as well as in the other works to be cited in this chapter, there will be considerable evidence of both medical practice and the theory which underlies it and on occasion undermines it. The case histories are themselves remarkable.

"Doctors bury their mistakes": the saying is old and common but has a suppressed clause, namely, they do not talk about their failures, not at least in public. So convinced of this is the lay public that when a doctor does "talk," the layman often cannot believe

that the talk is not inadvertent or "not for publication," as with
W. H. S. Jones who decided that the case histories in the Hippocratic Collection must have been "private information" (volume I,
p. 144). How else explain that of forty-two cases twenty-five
terminated in death? The "inadvertence" becomes "devotion to
truth" (*ibid.*), and again we have a feeling of lay shock. But conditions differed when these histories were written from those which
obtain today, and writing a book was not the "immediate public
act," the instant publicity that it would now be.

The first fourteen cases belong to the conclusion of Book I of
Epidemics. Twelve more cases form the beginning of Book III of
the same work, which closes with another group of sixteen cases.
The significance of these groupings (preserved by the manuscript
tradition) is uncertain. (*Epidemics* I and III are remarkable for the
very fact that names of actual persons are given: even without the
case histories Book I names in one way or another twenty-five different persons.) Incidentally, it is in chapter II of Book I of *Epidemics* that the deservedly famous statement is made which follows:
"With respect to diseases, you must observe these two things: Help
(if you can), or else Do no harm; Medicine involves three things:
the disease, the patient, and the physician; the physician is the helper
of the art of medicine; and the patient must cooperate with the physician in resisting his disease."

The locale of the cases histories in each group is various, but possibly all the patients in the first group were treated on the northern
Aegaean island of Thasos, the only place reference in the group
which is certain. There is a reference to Clazomenae, the Ionian
coastal town on the Bay of Smyrna, but the likelihood is that this
gives us merely the birthplace of the patient, not the locale of treatment. The other patients are generally referred to by their address
at the time of treatment: Philiscus lived near the Wall: Silenus lived
in the Flats near the property of Eualcidas; the wife of Epicrates
lay sick in bed near the (shrine or statue of the) Founder; Clean-
actides lay sick in bed just above the Shrine of Heracles; Erasinus
lived near the Ravine of Bootes; a Clazomenian lay sick near the
Well of Phrynichides; a woman lay sick on the beach; Melidia lay
sick near the Shrine of Hera. The two patients explicitly connected
with Thasos are the wife of Philinus (Case IV) and a man named
Crito (Case IX). In addition, a Herophon, a Meton, a Wife of

Dromeades, and one overheated citizen (*anthropos thermainome-nos*) are mentioned without reference to their addresses at all.

Group two, from the Third Book of *Epidemics,* has twelve individual case histories. Again, the only place name given is that of Thasos (as the dwelling place of a patient named Philistes: Case IV). Two patients, one an adolescent male, the other a woman in first childbirth, were confined to their beds in a picturesquely named quarter called the Liars' Market (*pseudeon agore*). Others include a man named Pythion, residing near the Shrine of Earth (*Ge*); Hermocrates who lay abed near the New Wall; an unnamed man who lay sick in the garden of Delearces; Chaerion, confined to bed in the home of Demaenetus (but the latter name is uncertain); the unmarried daughter of Euryanax, no address given; a woman confined to bed in the home of Aristion; another who was confined in the home of Tisamenos; a third woman who belonged to the household of Pantimides; and a Wife of Hicetas.

The sixteen cases in the third and last group of histories show much more variation of locale. Five of the sixteen cases belong to Thasos, including a man who came from Paros (Case I). To Abdera, a town on the southern coast of Thrace noted for the stupidity of its inhabitants as well as for the distinguished philosophers Protagoras and Democritus, belong six cases. Two cases (V and XII) developed in Larisa (but which Larisa or Larissa is impossible to say: Stephanus of Byzantium names eleven towns that bore this name on either side of the Aegaean Sea, two in Thessaly, others in Pelasgia, Ossa, the Troad, Aeolis, Syria, Lydia, Crete, Attica, Ephesus, and the acropolis of Argos). One case belongs to Cyzicus, the Mysian town on the Propontis (the Sea of Marmora). There is also one case from Meliboea, the birthplace in Thessaly of the mythical Philoctetes. Only in Case IV is the place name lacking (the patient, too, is anonymous).

The point of the foregoing is in part, of course, that the practitioner who wrote up these cases after treatment or during treatment moved from one locality to another in the course of his career, hence the term *periodeutes* ("traveler") applied to those of the medical profession by Galen. Thasos, of course, is off the Thracian coast, but it is not far from Thessaly, to which Larisa may belong and Meliboea does belong, while Abdera is in Thrace, which itself is not very distant from Cyzicus in the Propontis— in other words, all these cases which are tied to a specific place can be located in a fairly smallish segment of the semicircle of land bordering the upper Aegean, thereby giving us a topography not only for the cases mentioned but also for the man who wrote them down. This was the locus, in part, of his medical practice; it also does not debar him from being a native of Cos, if it was either Hippocrates or one of the Coan school who authored them, as seems most likely.

The form of citation in the third group also is of some interest. I have already referred to the native of Paros who became sick on Thasos and lay in bed on the other side of the Artemisium or Shrine of Artemis (Diana). Case II: a woman confined to bed near the Cold Water; again on Thasos, Pythion, sick in bed above the Shrine of Heracles; Case V, a Larisaean, described only as a bald man; Case VI: Abderite named Pericles, no address given; Case VII: Abderite girl confined by the Sacred Way; Case VIII: Abderite named Anaxion, confined to bed by the Thracian Gates; Case IX: Abderite, Heropythus, who lived near Up Street (Up Square?); Case X: Abderite named Nicodemus, no address; Case XI: an unnamed Thasian woman, residing on the Plain near the property of Pylades; Case XII: an unnamed Larisean girl, no address; Case XIII: an Abderite named Apollonius, no address; Case XIV: the primipara of Cyzicus, mentioned above, also no address; Case XV: wife of the Thasian Delearces, confined to a bed on the Plain; Case XVI: a young unnamed wastrel, without address, in Meliboea.

Almost all the cases were characterized by fever, but their etiology and symptomatology in other respects differed widely. It should also be emphasized that although the cases are included in two books of the work(s) called *Epidemics,* few if any were epidemic in nature, which indicates that these forty-two case histories were early attached to these two Books of the *Epidemics,* possibly because of the patient names which so atypically appear in Book I. The onset of illness in most cases is marked by the fever and or chills (*pyr; rhigos*), which so often appears to have been the first symptom noticed by the physician (and perhaps the patient, too). Occasionally, the first symptom noticed, however, was acute localized pain varying topically with individual patients. Very often the physician's first entry indicates his judgment as to the *cause* of the illness. For example, we have these statements: Group I, Case II (Silenus): illness noted after overexertion, drinking, and inappropriate time of exercise; Case IV (Wife of Philinus), two weeks postpartum illness developed in woman making normal recovery from childbirth; Case V (Wife of Epicrates), pre - and postpartum symptomatology; Case IX (the Thasian Crito), pain localized in big toe develops while patient was walking about; Case XI (Wife of Dromeades), two days postpartum chills and fever; Case XII (no name), male, who ate when overheated and drank too much; Case XIII (the woman on the beach), female three months pregnant, first symptom fever; Case XIV (Melidia), first symptoms violent pains in head, neck, and chest, followed by fever, then menstrual flow (slight).

Group II, Case I (Python), first symptom trembling of the hands, then acute fever; Case IV (Philistes), persistent headaches, then stupor, confinement to bed: pain worsened by heavy drinking which caused continuing fevers; Case V (Chaerion), fever develops after drinking; Case VII (female patient in household of Aristion), suffering from angina, develops indistinctness of speech; Case VIII (the young man resident near the Liars' Market), first symptom fever following unusual fatigue, effort, and drinking—or perhaps only the drinking was unusual; Case IX (female lodging with Tisamenos), first sympton inflammatory attack of the upper bowel; Case X (female in Pantimides' household), first symptom fever following miscarriage; Case XI (Wife of Hicetas), first symptom fever following miscarriage in the fifth month; Case XII (woman, primipara, resident near the Liars' Market), first symptom fever after painful delivery of a male child.

Group III, Case I (native of Paros, resident in Thasos), sick abed, seized by acute fever; Case II (Thasian woman, address Cold Water), three days post partum, first symptom fever and chills; Case III (Pythion, address above Shrine of Heracles), first symptoms chills and fever following exertion, fatigue, and careless living; Case IV (no name), patient suffering from phrenitis, first symptom vomiting, following by fever and chills; Case V (the bald Larisaean), sudden pain in right thigh, followed by fever (very much elevated); Case VI (the Abderite Pericles), first sympton acute fever; Case VII (Abderite girl), confined to bed, first sympton acute fever; Case VIII (Abderite Anaxion), first symptom acute fever; Case IX (Abderite Heropythus), cephalalgia, confinement to bed subsequently, developed acute fever; Case X (the Abderite Nicodemus), first sympton fever following sexual activity and drinking; Case XI

(Thasian female), irritable disposition following understandable grief, first symptoms loss of sleep and appetite, accompanied by thirst and nausea); Case XII (Larisaean girl), first symptom acute fever; Case XIII (the Abderite Apollonius), longstanding illness without confinement to bed, first symptoms swollen abdomen and constant pain in the liver region; Case XIV (female in Cyzicus), first symptom acute fever and chills following difficult labor (she had twin daughters) and very poor lochial discharge; Case XV (Wife of Delearces), first symptoms acute fever and chills following an emotional shock (*lype*—literally, a "grief"); Case XVI (the Meliboean adolescent male), overheating from drinking and sexual activity, followed by chills and fever, nausea, sleeplessness, and lack of thirst.

Many if not most of the patients named in the histories may have been slaves. There is no evidence that they were not treated as well as their betters, with complete disregard of social distinctions on the part of the physician who attended them. The question is discussed by Fridolf Kudlien in a recent essay, "Die Sklaven in der griechischen Medizin der klassischen and hellenistischen Zeit."

After brief identification of the patient and the initial symptoms discovered at the time, presumably, of the writer's first visit (the Greek term for which is *epidemia*, which is also used in the sense of English "epidemic"), each history adheres to the same pattern of observations: successive visits were made during the course of the illness, but the record shows only observations made at particular intervals which vary from daily to gaps of as much as one or two weeks. Visits were probably on a regular, perhaps even daily basis, but the histories indicate the writer's preoccupation with noting the times and symptoms of "crisis," hence the rather frequent omission of mention of intervening visits or observations.

It is clear from the histories and the adjoining table that the writer was what we would call a general practitioner. The histories include grown men and women, as well as boys and girls. Babies and possibly aged persons are not included. The majority of cases show nontraumatic disease processes, but some may have developed as a consequence of trauma or injury. The treatment is only infrequently indicated, but what is indicated seems to have been of a conservative nature, more palliative than radical. There is some likelihood that in certain cases the patients were discovered in the streets or public ways or even in the fields in the countryside

TABULAR SUMMARY OF THE 42 CASE HISTORIES

Group	Case	Place	Age	Sex	Status	Duration in Days	Recovered	Died
I	1			M	?	6		x
	2		20	M	?	11		x
	3			M	?	17	x	
	4	Thasos		F	free	20		x
	5			F	free	80	x	
	6			M	?	80	x	
	7			M	?	5	x	
	8			M	?	5		x
	9	Thasos		M	?	2		x
	10			M	?	40	x	
	11			F	free	6		x
	12			M	?	11		x
	13			F	?	14	x	
	14			F	?	11	x	
II	1			M	?	50	x(?)	
	2			M	?	27		x
	3			M	?	40	x	
	4	Thasos		M	?	5		x
	5			M	?	20	x	
	6		child	F	free	7		x
	7			F	?	5		x
	8		20	M	?	7		x
	9			F	?	—		x
	10			F	slave?	7		x
	11			F	free	7		x
	12		17	F	slave?	14		x
III	1	Thasos		M	slave?	120		x
	2	Thasos		F	slave?	80		x
	3	Thasos		M	slave?	10		x
	4			M	slave?	4		x
	5	Larisa		M	slave?	4		x
	6	Abdera		M	?	4	x	
	7	Abdera	child	F	slave?	27	x	
	8	Abdera		M	slave?	34	x	
	9	Abdera		M	free?	120	x	
	10	Abdera		M	slave?	24	x	
	11	Thasos		F	slave?	3	x	
	12	Larisa	child	F	slave?	6	x	
	13	Abdera		M	free?	34		x
	14	Cyzicus		F	slave?	17		x
	15	Thasos		F	free?	21		x
	16	Meliboea	youth	M	slave?	24		x

Totals:
    Thasos: 8 cases; more probably
    Abdera: 6 cases
    Larisa: 2 cases
    Cyzicus: 1 case
    Meliboea: 1 case
    Males: 25; Females: 17
    Children: 3; Adolescents: 4
    Freeborn: 8 (probable or possible)—(2 or more of foreign extraction)
    Slave: 14 (probable); 20 (possible)
    Longest case recorded: 120 days (2 cases)
    Shortest case recorded: 2 days (1 case)
    Recoveries: 17 (including 1 probable recovery)
    Deaths: 25
    Pregnancies: 9 (including 2 miscarriages)
    First menses: 2
    Venereal disease: 1 (possible gonorrhea)

Note: The diagnosis of several cases is probable from the information
    given in the histories, but possibly none is beyond question.)

from which they may have been removed to the nearest place of
lodging while undergoing treatment. There is reference to the
presence of attendants and evidence that such were available is
inferable from the several references to condition of patients and
changes that may have occurred during the night.

The commonest treatment referred to in these histories is the administration of cathartics, "clysters," suppositiories, and in two instances of childbirth the application of a pessary to relieve pain
(*sic*). In Case VII Group I, mention is made of bathing the
patient's head. In Case VIII, Group III, the Abderite Anaxion was
bled in the arm apparently to relieve right side pain (which it
did succeed in doing, but a dry cough persisted), and also was
given warm applications. But the majority of cases (thirty out of
forty-two) make no mention of treatment at all. Always, the focus
of emphasis is the weathering of critical days, as they were called.
The coincidence of important changes with the "critical days" (odd
or even) is stated more than once. One very common symptom
mentioned is that of convulsions, but there is never any indication
of the therapy prescribed to counter them.

A common feature of the histories is the mention of emotional
states of the patients, as well as the degree of disorientation in-

duced by the course of illness. Rest or lack of it is carefully noted and there is scrupulous observation of all discharges in successive stages of the disease process: urine, feces, sweating, flatus, mucous discharge, pus formation, etc., are always described accurately and evaluated. Color, consistency, smell, and quantity are regularly and carefully recorded. Respirations are described beautifully. Tenderness (rebound?) of viscera is noted as well as rigidities and swellings wherever they appear. Sleep and coma are differentiated. Talkativeness or unusual silence is also recorded. Fears, depressions, and instances of delirium or wild talking, incoherence, and states of withdrawal are all set down. Everywhere the histories are marked by acuity of observation and objectivity of statement without exception. Taken together, the forty-two case histories are one of the most impressive documents in any literature, ancient or modern. In some instances, there are summary remarks which may also include reference to symptoms omitted from the record of critical days. Several histories end with the phrases *krisis* or *teleos ekrithe,* meaning "resolution" or "complete crisis" and signifying recovery.

II   *The Variety of Treatment*

Therapy in the Hippocratic writings is most often modest, restrained, and conservative from our point of view. This is entirely consistent with the previously mentioned injunction, "To help or at least to cause no harm" (*askein peri ta nosemata dyo, ophelein e me blaptein*). The most favored diets prescribed for the seriously ill included barley soup (called *ptisane*), barley water (*chylos*), honey and water (*hydromeli*), or vinegar and honey (*oxymeli*), the merits and demerits of which for specific symptom relief are extensively discussed in several chapters of *Regimen in Acute Diseases* (*Peri diaites oxeon*). Hot applications for topical relief of pain, called *thermasmata,* were recommended. The instruments used resembled our hot water bottles: skins, bladders, but also containers of bronze or earthenware, with the precaution that some soft material be applied first to prevent discomfort (and, presumably, to avoid burning the patient). A sponge soaked in hot water and then wrung out might also be used for the purpose: it should be covered to prevent evaporation and prolong the warming effect, according to the directions given. Dry materials were also used in topical applications; specifically mentioned are warmed salt and millet (chapter 21).

Venesection or bloodletting (*tome*) was used for relief of pain, if heat applications failed, and the author recommends prolonging this treatment until the color of the blood changed (chapter 22).

For relief of pain below the diaphragm, the physician would recommend for cathartic black hellebore (*Helleborus niger*) or peplium (*Euphorbia peplus*), mixed with a variety of fragrant herbs. The physical properties of each mixture is evaluated with the purpose and effect of each clearly in mind. Purgation by emetic or cathartic of course is one of the commonest treatments mentioned (chapter 23).

Occasionally, food is withheld entirely. The indications for such treatment are carefully discussed, but more often nourishment was not forbidden, only reduced in amount (chapter 25). In any case, he thought it much safer to avoid abrupt changes in diet. In the same chapter (28) we find the statement that the training of the physician ought to include the proper regime for healthy individuals. (We still have a short *Regimen in Health* by a Hippocratic writer.) Rest and exercise are also prescribed, always in the context of what might be appropriate for the individual patient (chapter 29). The effects of various solids and liquids in the diet, of meat, bread, pancakes, wine, water, as well as spices are carefully noted. Distinctions in use of the various wines (sweet, light, dark, etc.) depend on their effects. He defends the use of hydromel (honey and water) which may have been as unpopular then as castor oil in more recent times. He has reservations about the use of water in the diet but its use is at times indicated (chapter 63), *e.g.,* whenever the brain is affected or there is extreme heaviness of the head. Other drinks for the sick included herbal drinks, and those obtained from raisins, grapeskins, wheat, safflower, myrtle, and pomegranates (*rhoie*), but their description has not survived (chapter 64).

The last chapters of *Regimen in Acute Disease* (65–68) are devoted to bathing of the patient. Its recommendations are wise, sensible, and interesting.

Frequency of bathing depends of course on the condition of the patient as well as his preference. Sometimes the physician encounters the situation in which facilities are wanting for proper bathing, so it has to be restricted; equipment and attendants may be wanting, too. The last named may be among the original references to nursing, and analogous if not to our professional nurses in this instance, to the modern licensed practical nurse, or to the orderly. I have discussed this more fully elsewhere in an article which has appeared in the *American Journal of Nursing* (December, 1965). A kind of soap consisting of a paste prepared from olive oil and an alkali and called *smegma* could be used but the author recommends little rubbing with it and careful removal with tepid water, using sponges instead of scrapers, and avoiding chill to the patient. Bathing soon after a meal is discouraged. Contraindications to bathing altogether are also given, but daily bathing is all right where the benefit is apparent. The effects of salt and fresh water, hot and cold, are noted in *Regimen Book II,* chapter 57.

A long list of foods other than those mentioned above is discussed in the middle chapters of *Regimen,* Book II, and the nutritive and curative value of each of the foodstuffs is given. Grains are mentioned in chapters 39–44 and include barley, wheat, bran of various cereals, spelt, and oats, as well as millet groats and husks. Vegetables include beans (*kyamoi*), peas, chickpeas, lentils, bitter vetch; linseed or clary seed, lupins, and the seeds of hedge mustard, cucumbers, sesame, wild saffron, and black and white poppy were thought worthy of mention as edibles (chapter 65).

Meats included the flesh of cattle, goats, swine, lambs, sheep, asses, horses, dogs (including puppies!), wild boars, deer, hares, foxes, and hedgehogs (chapter 46).

A few birds are listed: ringdoves, partridges, pigeons, roosters, turtledoves, geese, ducks, and marsh or water fowl (chapter 47).

Fish include scorpion fish, dragon fish (great weever), callionymos, piper, grey fish, perch, thrissa, thrush fish, hake, gudgeon, elephitis (?), torpedo, skate, turbot, mullet, cestreus; eels, polypus, cuttle, shellfish, pinna, limpet, purple fish, trumpet, and oysters, mussels, cockles, tellines, sea nettles, urchin spawn, spiny lobsters, sea crabs, among the marine foods (chapter 48).

These are only some of the edible substances mentioned in *Regimen,* there are several dozen others, including a long list of fruits and vegetables which I omit from listing here: the main aspect considered is their digestibility.

Exercise is the subject of chapters 61–66 of *Regimen,* Book II, with which the book closes. The term used for exercise(s) is *ponoi* (elsewehere used of labor, pains, and exertions). He distinguishes between "natural" (*kata physin*) and "violent" (*dia bies*) exercises, but the distinction would be strange to us: natural exercises are activities of sight, hearing, speech, and thought. He cannot quite decide whether *walking* is natural or violent and does distinguish among several different kinds of walking, partly by times of day, and partly by its incidence after meals and gymnastics. The laxative effect of walking is noted and an explanation of it attempted which is not now convincing (chapter 62).

Running (*dromoi*) is recommended, especially for heavy eaters and particularly in winter (chapter 63). Even the track is evaluated, according to three types in use: single, double, and circular (the best for weight reduction was the single track of adjustable length, but the double and especially the circular track were better for getting rid of flabbiness).

Arm swinging is not recommended: too apt to cause sprains! But shadow boxing (*anakinemata*) and pushups (*anakouphismata*) invigorate both body and soul. Wrestling and rubbing tend to harden the body and are said to make for growth in the exterior parts. Different kinds of wrestling are mentioned with their various effects. Hand (-to-hand?) wrestling also tends to tighten up the flesh, as do use of the punching bag and arm exercises. Apparently, holding the breath (*pneumatos kataschesis*) was thought to be of value on occasion, too.

Pain of fatigue from exercise (called *kopoi*) is discussed in terms of the condition of the individual. Prior habituation makes all the difference, as the lengthy consideration of this topic shows. The following prescription is given for a fever which develops after immoderate exercise: first bathe the patient moderately in warm water, administer soft wine (*malthakos oinos*), follow with a hearty dinner of several courses, wine again, rest, then the patient should vomit (*sic!*), walk for a bit, and finally sleep on a soft bed; six days are then devoted to restoring the patient gradually to his normal habits of food intake and exercise. All the features of this regimen are justified by the explanations given in the concluding portion of chapter 66. The greatest emphasis is placed on gradualness in the changes fostered by the treatment.

Incidentally, the dehydrative effect of vomiting is explicitly denied: the explanation is curious and perhaps confused in the manuscript tradition (chapter 59). Emetics were prescribed on a regular basis for persons in good health; possibly, the underlying notion was that of a certain toxicity in even the normal functioning of the alimentary canal (*Regimen,* Book III, chapter 68).

Seasonal variations in diet and exercise for various ages and "constitutions" (*katastaseis*) are prescribed in the same chapter. In winter, for example, only a single meal a day should be eaten, and sexual activity for older men should be increased more than for the younger.

The ill-effects of sleeping after a heavy meal are explained (chapter 71) and the discomfort attributed in part to a perturbation of the soul: the individual thinks he is struggling; such a condition is symptomatic of approaching illness.

As might be expected, a great deal of space is given to the digestive process particularly as it affects bowel function, in both the well and unwell (especially in chapters 79–83, and *passim* elsewhere in the three Books of *Regimen,* and in fact the entire Hippocratic corpus).

The fourth book of *Regimen* is often referred to by its subtitle, *Dreams* (*Peri enhypnion*). Since modern notions about dreams and their content are based almost exclusively on Freud's *Interpretation of Dreams,* the reader will be surprised and disappointed by the absence of such ideas in the Hippocratic work—if, indeed, it is Hippocratic in origin. The question arises chiefly because it is the only work in the Collection which attributes significance to divine intervention in ill-health and specifically prescribes prayer.[2] The explanation of dream activity with which *Dreams* begins is interesting, and I give a translation of it here:

Whoever has a correct understanding of the signs found in dreams, will realize that they have considerable effect on everything. The reason for this is that the soul is subservient to the waking body, dividing its attention to many things, and therefore is not its own mistress, but devotes part of its attention to each sense or function of the body—to hearing, seeing, touching, walking, and actions involving the whole body; whereas thought is never independent. However, when the body is at rest, the soul, moving and awake, manages its own proper sphere, and by itself performs all the activities of the body. Now the body itself, when asleep, does not perceive, whereas the soul, when awake, is fully conscious of everything and can see whatever is visible, and hear whatever is audible, walks, touches, is sensitive to pain, and capable of serious thought. In short, the soul discharges all the bodily functions when the body sleeps. Whoever, therefore, has a correct understanding of these facts and their interpretation, understands also a major part of wisdom.[3]

Two classes of dreams are distinguished by the writer. One class consist of dreams which are divine in origin and foretell good or evil to states and individuals. The other class indicate in advance physical changes in the body. The writer reserves to physicians the latter class of dreams owing to the specialized ignorance of dream interpreters who have no medical knowledge. These interpreters (*kritai ton enhypnion*) recommend precautions to be taken without instructions; instead, they merely recommend prayer to the gods. The writer says prayer is a good thing, but one who calls upon the gods for help should also contribute his own effort (*kai to men euchesthai agathon; dei de kai auton sullambanonta tous theous epikaleisthai*).

Of course, there is a common connection between ancient and modern dream interpretation, namely the necessity of explaining the disturbing, upsetting, threatening, or oppressive nature of (some) dreams and the more or less superficially puzzling character of most if not all of them. So, with the Hippocratic (?) writer, the object is to explore the meaning of both good and bad "signs" (*tekmeria*). (Cf. modern contrast of "latent" and "manifest" meaning.)

Good signs are those which repeat the images of thoughts and actions done or planned normally during the day, and they give an indication of good health as well "because the soul stays with the plans of the day." Dreams which show conflict with these plans and purposes, with struggle or triumph, indicate a disturbance in the body. The writer does not recommend or infer from such dreams a particular course of action or decision, but he does recommend treatment of the body. *The psychic disturbance is said to be caused by a secretion (apokrisis) resulting from an excess or repletion (plesmone).*

So much is not so bad, but most of the signs are connected with the appearance of heavenly bodies, which is where ancient and modern notions must part company. Propitious signs call for the appropriate regimen and prayers to the Sun, to Zeus Ouranios, to Zeus Ktesios (protector of house and property), to Athena Ktesie, to Hermes, and to Apollo. Malignant signs call for prayer to the apotropaic gods (averters of evil), to Earth, and to the Heroes (chapter 89).

Black objects indicate more serious and more dangerous diseases, whereas new or unfamiliar objects indicate a change (chapter 91). Here, of course, an ordinary sort of association is evident. Crossing rivers, enemy soldiers, and monsters of strange shape indicate disease or delirium. The symbolic powers of these interpretations seem weak indeed compared to the modern.

There is no evidence of recognition of guilt and anxiety processes, of transformations, repression, suppression, or displacement and substitution in *Dreams*. The prescriptions given are limited to dietotherapy, baths, purgatives, and exercise. There is no attempt to associate the dream material with emotional or functional problems instead of merely organic or somatic states.

III   *Epilepsy, The "Sacred Disease"*

Epilepsy is an impressive disease, more awesome and shocking to the beholder perhaps than the disease itself or the pathology underlying its complex and highly various syndrome warrants. An entire "book" was devoted to its consideration by one of the Hippocratic writers and entitled in the original *Peri hieres nousou (On the Sacred Disease)*. It is one of the most estimable works in the entire collection. It alone would give distinction and value to the ancient medicine just as it far surpasses in judgment, accuracy, and wisdom the medicine of both the Middle Ages and the Renaissance.

The suddenness of epilepsy, with its attendant loss of consciousness or convulsions, or both, and the dramatic character of the visible attacks must have given rise to its familiar name of "sacred disease," "sacred" meaning "accursed" or "taboo," as well as implying a "visitation" of some god or other. The author of *Epilepsy* is at great pains to disassociate the disease entity, the reality of it, from popular, widely accepted notions about it, which clothed the attacks in dread and superstition, and above all from the wrongheaded belief that it was caused by a god. The best way was to show that it was no more and no less divine than any other disease, that it had a nature and a cause like all other diseases. It is in fact, he says, no more wonderful than any other of many diseases to which the same adjective might apply. Once this is understood, the emptiness of the usual superstition-ridden treatment by means of purifications (*katharmoi*) and incantations (*epaoidai*) will be recognized, neither of which is a sacred, pious, or divine means of healing, but on the contrary the practitioners who use such means are themselves impious and unholy. He shrewdly observes that the irrational conception of the disease prevents rational treatment of those who suffer from it, while in fact the patients improve or deteriorate according to the treatment which they actually do get. Something in man's nature makes him ascribe the blame (or cause) for all sorts of poorly understood events to one god or another. (For example, imitating a goat, roaring, and having right-side convulsions are popularly ascribed to the Mother of the Gods, and foaming at the mouth and kicking are blamed on Ares.)

The superstitious treatment of epilepsy included purification with blood by a kind of sympathetic magic, or the defilement is hidden away to prevent its contaminating others. But a god, being perfectly holy, is perfectly incapable of causing defilement in bodies that are perfectly corruptible anyway; rather, the god would cause purity and sanctity even in those who harbor the worst and most unholy sins; so runs the argument against the superstitious.

The writer was convinced that the disease was curable (*pathos ieton*), provided that it had not become chronic and so resistant to remedy (*pharmaka*). Its origin, like that of other diseases, is hereditary in nature (*kata genos*). He thought it attacked those who are naturally phlegmatic rather than the choleric ("bilious," according to the humoral theory).

The source of epilepsy is to be found in the brain. Following this statement the author gives a good, if somewhat superficial, description of the brain. Further, the disease is congenital, since it develops in the embryo from a failure in the removal of impurities. (Hereditary and congenital aspects are apparently confused in the account.)

The dynamic cause of epilepsy is given as the diversion of phlegm to the veins and the heart (*sic*)—evidently he thought the head veins were so affected too. A result of this is the enlarged beating of the heart with attendant dyspnoea and orthopnoea (inability to breathe comfortably except in erect posture). A typical attack is described as follows: the patient becomes speechless and chokes, a foam or froth flows from the mouth, the patient gnashes his teeth and clenches his hands spasmodically; his eyes turn without coordination, he loses consciousness, and may become unable to control his bowels. The process by which each symptom appears is then explained. Kicking is another symptom. In severe cases, the fit may terminate in death. A strong onset of the disease in young children may also cause death. A child who recovers from an attack may bear the marks of it in some distortion of the affected part, usually the mouth, eye, hand, or neck Or the child outgrows the disease and is no longer subject to such attacks. He may also risk worsening of the disease if proper countermeasures are not taken. The disease is said to be not fatal in older persons except in rare instances. In each category the explanation is referred to the nature of the flows (fluxes, from *katarrhoos*) of phlegm to the wrong vessels. Seasonal changes are said to affect those predisposed to such attacks. Patients twenty years old outgrow the disease unless it was evidenced at *birth;* their greater resistance is attributed to their having veins filled with lots of blood.

The disease was thought by the author to be endemic in domestic animals as well as in man, but especially common among goats, in which he thought to detect the presence of the disease by dissection of the heads, which were moist, dropsical, and smelly.

He also remarks on the fact that patients accustomed to the disease can anticipate their attacks and will seek to run away and hide from sight, where their falling may not be observed. This tendency to covering up or concealment he ascribes to a feeling of shame (*aischyne*) at their affliction; he denies that it might be because of fear of a god, as apparently most people supposed. Young children, unaccustomed at first to their ailment, fall where they are stricken, but when the presentiment of attack is developed, they will run to their mothers or a familiar person, in fear and terror of their suffering, because they do not yet know the feeling of shame. A better description is not to be found even in the novelist Dostoevsky.

It is in chapter 17 that the centrality of the brain is asserted. "Men must know," he says, "that the brain alone is the source of our pleasures, happiness, laughter, and jests, as well as our griefs, sorrows, anxieties, and lamentation." It is the instrument that enables us to see, hear, to distinguish between ugly and beautiful, bad and good, pleasant and unpleasant. It can inspire madness, delirium, dread, fear, sleeplessness, unseasonable mistakes, unfocused anxiety, absent-mindedness, and uncustomary action, all produced from the condition of the brain, as madness is from its moistness (*hygrotes*), whereas the individual is normal and sensible when the brain is stable (*hoson d' an atremese ho enkephalos*). It has the greatest power of all the organs in the human body, since in health it serves as the inter-

preter of perceptible phenomena from the air, even as it is air
which gives the brain its intelligence. Eyes, ears, tongue, hands,
and feet depend on the conscious perception of the brain (*phronesis*) for their action, and the whole body shares this intelligence
insofar as it shares the air. To conscious perception the brain is the
messenger and interpreter (chapters 19 and 20). The notion is
all the more impressive because it was a departure from widely
held notions about the center of awareness and intellection. He
refutes those who would assign it to the diaphragm or the heart,
misconceptions all the more common because of the physical sen-
sations commonly associated with either emotional or mental states—
notions, of course, which are not dead yet, since both stomach and
heart are popular favorites still in situating "gut reactions"—scarcely
conceivable without the mediating brain. Hence the diseases which
attack the brain are characterized as the most acute, the most
serious, the most (often) fatal, and the most difficult to judge
for those who are inexperienced.

Finally, he tells us that there is no necessity to classify epilepsy
uniquely or to look upon it as more divine than any other disease,
all diseases being equally divine and human, each with its own
nature and power unto itself, just as none of them is hopeless or
incurable. Understanding of disease processes and knowledge of
curative properties make quite unnecessary recourse to purifications
and magic (reading *mageie*) or quackery (if the reading is
banausie).

IV   *Sickness and Disease*

Several works in the Hippocratic Collection have the common
subject of therapeutics and are possibly if not probably by different
hands. Although the subject is shared, the point of departure and
the point of view vary with the contents of each work. There is no
significant distinction between *nousos* and *pathos* as used in the
titles of these essays in which, as in the rest of the corpus, the sense
of both is "disease," "sickness," "illness," though *pathos* from its
original meaning of "suffering" and "mischance" may at times be
better translated by the word "affliction." The main works in this
category which I consider here are *Disease,* Books I–II–III (*Peri
nouson, to proton, to deuteron, to triton*), and I have chosen
Illnesses to distinguish *Peri pathon* from the preceding (the former
"work" is not of one piece, however, as Littré noted, vol. I, p. 359

and elsewhere in the brief introduction to each Book); and, finally, *Internal Medicine* (*Peri ton entos pathon*). As might be expected, there is much duplication of content and discussion, which I will avoid here. Instead, the following will give some conspectus of disease states mentioned in the various works and their treatment, where indicated, since exhaustive treatment is both unnecessary and precluded by the space at my disposal. The essays are taken up in the order mentioned above.

Internal disease is said to originate with the humoral bile and phlegm, whereas external disease is caused by strain, wounds, and excess of heat, cold, dryness, or moisture (*Diseases, I,* chapter 2). A cautionary word is in order concerning the terminology used here. As much as possible, I have used the terms which appear in the original, only anglicized; they are not necessarily those in use in modern medicine, and the exact interpretation of several is debatable.

Several types of lung inflammation (*peripleumonie*) and empyemas are discussed in Book I, chapters 11–16. Most of the discussion is explanatory of the disease process. The only treatment which is mentioned explicitly is opening the veins in the arms (bloodletting) and a diet aimed at "drying out" the patient as well as reducing blood level (chapter 14).

Empyema of the gut (*koilie*) is described and potter's earth recommended as a drying agent (chapter 17)—compare the modern use of kaolin, the fine white clay of Chinese origin.

Penetrating wounds of the chest are described (chapters 21-22) in great detail, but no treatment is specifically mentioned, and the chief emphasis is on interpreting the signs which indicate recovery or death.

The symptoms of chills and fever are described, but again treatment is not mentioned (chapters 23-24); likewise, sweating (chapter 25).

Pleurisy and lung inflammation are described, and under certain conditions vein incision is recommended (in the arm, either the vein called splenic or the vein called hepatic) in chapters 26–28.

Causus, defined as a bilious remittent fever endemic in the eastern Mediterranean, is described without reference to treatment (chapter 29), as is the case with *phrenitis* or inflammation of the brain (chapter 30).

Book II of *Diseases* places much more emphasis on treatment and less on description of the disease process.

It is not unlikely, in numerous instances, that when treatment is not mentioned, the disease would run its course fatal or otherwise, in which case the role of the physician may have been simply to mark the significant signs and days of "crisis." More likely, palliative treatment *was* given. So for some of the illnesses discussed in the opening chapters of *Diseases,* Book II, for which again no treatment is described: a phlegmatic disease with dysuria and amblyopia; phlegmatic ulcers of the head; acute cerebral infection, with sharp pain, bilious vomiting, dysuria, and delirium, or with purulent discharge from nostrils and mouth; sphacelism (gangrene) of the brain (but the symptoms noted fail to make the terminological use clear); cephalalgia with sudden loss of speech and control of movement, followed (*sic*) by apoplexy and paralysis, ascribed possibly to excessive drinking of wine; *teredo* (caries or necrosis of flesh and bone of the skull, said not to be fatal); apoplexy, or softening of the brain, with semi-coma and incontinence; angina, with difficult salivation, dyspnoea, and occasionally fever; staphylitis (inflammation of the uvula) with necrosis of soft tissue, but this time surgical intervention is prescribed; disease involving the tonsils (*antiades*), hypoglottis, gums, or tongue (chapters 1-11). But for some of these the treatment is noted later.

For a complex syndrome of swelling in the head, with polyuria, strangury, reduced vision, thickening of the skin, and dullness of hearing, the treatment prescribed was as follows: shave the head, apply a hot water bottle (actually made of leathern hide), as hot as can be safely tolerated and repeat until pain subsides, provided the patient does not weaken, in which case heat treatment should be interrupted, with purgative for the intestines and use of a diuretic (*melikreton,* honey mixed with water), barley-water, and a whole series of dietary adaptations (chapter 12). As the disease progresses, the treatment becomes more and more heroic: after forty days, purgation of head and bowels, then wait for seven days, and if relapse occurs, have the patient take a steam bath, administer hellebore (described now as a "cardiac and arterial tonic, diuretic and cathartic"), again purgation of head and bowels, and finally, cauterization by pairs of eschars, eight in number: two by the ears, two at the temples, one on either side of the nape of the neck, and one on each wing or flange of the nostrils! These are the means by which health is restored.

For ulcers of the head, mentioned above, purgation is recommended by steaming and use of hot water, followed by purgation again, diet of whey or asses' milk, the patient being kept on a reduced and laxative diet, with bathing forbidden for a time; two kinds of ointment are given with the ingredients carefully listed; periodic use of emetics over several weeks; again, the head may be shaved, and incisions (small) made in the skin, with application of an oily woolen compress soaked in wine, to be followed in succession by an oil, then powder of cypress, but keeping the compress in place until recovery.

For a cephalalgia (otitis?), with vomiting, dysuria, and delirium, among other features of treatment is a pack for the ears made from "silver flower" (*argyrou anthos*), sandarache (red sulphide of arsenic), and psimythion (white lead), in equal parts, finely ground; hot sponges and steaming are also recommended.

For a case of "water on the brain" resistant to conservative treatment trepanation (trephination) of the skull is indicated. There is no evidence of hesitation to employ surgical means, when others fail (chapter 15).

For another type of head infection or inflammation, bleeding the head is directed; the illness followed a fever and was accompanied by chills and pain, nausea, with inability to rest and delirium from the pain; the causative fever is termed *lipyrie,* defined as a malignant remittent fever (possibly malarial in nature, but the term used is apparently not modern).

For a case of vertigo without fever, an incision was made in the scalp from the hairline in front to the hairline in back of the head and powdered with fine salt; the incision was closed with a double thread, a compress of wax mixed with pitch was then applied, then an oily woolen cloth, and a bandage on top, to remain in place for seven days unless the pain persisted (chapter 18).

Celery juice (*selinou chylos*) was injected into the nostrils for another head ailment; in the same type of ailment, flower of copper and myrrh were applied subsequently to the nostrils: whatever the ailment may have been, it is called not fatal (chapter 10).

For the severe illness called sphacelism of the brain, referred to above, an attempt was made to reduce the flow of blood to the head by means of tight compresses; the writer notes that recovery from this illness is rare (chapter 20).

For a case of "stroke," hot baths and honey mixed with water (*melikreton*) and served warm were used, with purgations, but again few survive the initial attack (chapter 21).

Loss of speech and fever following extreme intoxication called for hot baths, sponging with hot water, and the insertion of peeled onions or *krommya* into the nostrils, apparently to induce the patient to rouse from sleep and to talk; subsequently, sleep is good for him and lights should be removed from his room and no talking to him permitted; the rest of the treatment is dietary.

For a case of angina, cleaning of the throat was achieved first by steaming with a complex decoction of many ingredients and if necessary by scraping the sides of the throat with a branch of myrtle wrapped in soft wool—much like the modern swabs wrapped in cotton batten (chapter 26). This too is characterized as a dangerous disease with high mortality.

The gargling (*gargarismos*) referred to just above was aided by a compound composed of origanon, mountain rue (*peganon*), savory (*thymbra*), celery, mint, and a small amount of sodium carbonate (*litron* or *nitron*). To this were added honey-and-water (*melikreton*) and a little vinegar (*oxos*), and the whole then heated.

For an inflammation of the under tongue and the epiglottis, a paste of green mint, celery, origanon, sodium carbonate, red sumac, the whole ground together and then dipped in honey, was rubbed on the affected parts (chapter 28).

Cauterization was done on a palatal tumor (chapter 32) with sodium carbonate and warm water, then wine used, to cleanse and perhaps disinfect the wound.

Nasal polyps were removed with a thread and sponge (chapter 33). Very careful instructions are given for their use. For other polyps in the same area cauterization was used (chapter 34). Occasionally, polyps involved incision of the nasal cartilage with a bistoury (long bladed knife) and closure of the wound by cautery (chapter 36). An ointment was applied to promote healing; lead (*molybdos*) is also prescribed.

For a condition resembling cancer in the nose, cauterization was used too, and followed by powdering with hellebore (chapter 37).

For *icterus* or jaundice bloodletting is prescribed underneath the tongue; then, after bathing the area in warm water, the patient is put on a liquid diet derived from asphodel roots, carefully rinsed, and cooked in wine, with a handful of celery leaves. Chickpeas, celery, and onions were included in the subsequent diet, along with specific types and quantities of wine; a cholagogue (agent promoting flow of bile into the intestines) was recommended as a purge, as well as asses' milk or whey, for his diet (chapter 38). For other cases of icterus, diuretics and cathartics were prescribed (chapter 39).

Tertian fever: purgation of bowels after the fourth attack; patient to drink about cne-eighth cf a pint of powdered root of cinquefoil (*Potentilla reptans*) in water. If this failed, another drink, this time of trefoil or treacle clover (*Psoralea bituminosa*), and some silphium juice in wine cut one half with water. The patient was then put to bed and covered to induce sweating. After sweating, he could if thirsty have a gruel of barley-groats and water. In the evening he might dine on cooked millet (a kind of porridge) with wine; he was to remain on a very soft diet as long as the fever lasted (chapter 42).

For quartan fever there are more things to do: evacuating the bowels, purging the head, and again evacuating the bowels; for persistent cases there were hot baths to be taken, and a drink composed in small quantities of hensbane (*Hyoscyamus niger*), mandragora, silphium, and trefoil or clover in a medium of unmixed wine. Other items prescribed in the regime were steam baths, garlic dipped in honey, a dish of lentils, honey, and vinegar (to induce vomiting); rinse after vomiting, then, refreshed, the patient could take *cyceon* (*kykeon*, a dish contrived from barley groats, grated cheese, and wine, though other ingredients might be substituted) and water. Sweating was induced and other vomitants used; very soft diet prescribed and no medication while fasting (chapter 43).

Among the other afflictions for which treatment is prescribed in this second Book of Diseases are pleurisy (chapters 44–46), lung inflammations, pulmonary abscesses, pus in the chest, traumatic paracentesis (chapter 47), phthisis (chapters 48–53), fever with pulmonary involvement (chapter 54), a chronic pulmonary "erysipelas" (chapter 55), acute respiratory infection (chapter 56), pleural tumor with abscess (chapter 60), lethargus (chapter 65), "murderous" fever (*pyretos phonodes,* chapter 67), an illness marked by eructations (chapter 60), a disease called simply "phlegmatic" (chapter 70), leukophlegmasia (chapter 71), the "black sickness," which in spite of the severity of the symptoms given in the description, is presumably *not* to be confused with the "black plague" (chapter 73), and another of the same name but different in symptomatology (chapter 74).

Diseases, II, chapter 59, in discussing a condition described as the collapse cf the lung into the pleural cavity, is the source of the remark that there is a crepitation as of leather at the site upon auscultation. Auscultation itself, of the respiratory organs, was a discovery of the Hippocratics which was subsequently forgotten until its rediscovery by the French physician, René Théophile Hyacinthe Laënnec, whose classic work on the subject was published in 1819 under the title *Traité de l'auscultation médiate.*

Most cf *Diseases,* III is merely a redaction or repetition of the content of II, in part *verbatim.* There are, however, four diseases or conditions discussed in it which are not found in the supposedly precedent Book. These are tetanus, opisthotonus, ileus, and a more generalized section on fevers. The treatment for relief of the patient suffering from the severe symptoms of tetanus (who could look to recovery if he survived the first week or two) included pills of pepper and black hellebore in a bouillon, fat and hot, of fowl, in addition to which strong emetics were administered repeatedly and also steam baths, or hot applications topically at the points of pain. (chapter 12).

Opisthotonus, a tetanic spasm in which the body is arched like a bow and rests on the head and heels, called for the same treatment as for tetanus, but additionally one might use cold water (plunges or soaks) in abundance, covering the body with light, clean, warm blankets or perhaps clothing (chapter 13).

Ileus (*eileos*), defined now as an intestinal colic, and more explicitly as a "mechanical or adynamic obstruction of the bowel attended with severe colicky pain, vomiting, and often fever and dehydration" (*Stedman's Medical Dictionary*)—it is remarkable, incidentally, that this modern definition is in every point in accord with the syndrome described in the Hippocratic account—was relieved by immediate use of emetics, bleeding the head and the arm at the elbow (the purpose of the latter was to reduce the heating of the upper belly or stomach). The lower belly was warmed by placing the patient in a hot sitz bath, by constant anointing, and use of hot wet packs; using a suppository of honey ten fingers deep, and smearing the fundament with bull's bile; forcing air into the belly by means of a copper or bronze bellows (*physa chalkeutike*) to dilate the contracted belly and intestine; after the air was removed, the next treatment was an enema, plugged in by a sponge introduced into the rectum, the enema to be retained while the sitz bath was repeated, after which the patient could have honey and wine unmixed with water as nourishment. A supervening fever was considered fatal in ileus cases (chapter 14).

Chapter 17 provides a list of various cooling drinks for the use of patients suffering from malignant remittent fever (*kausos,* or causus), with the properties and virtues of each preparation carefully set forth, and the caution that the choice of drink must be determined in each case individually. A pint of honey was softened in water and mixed till sweet, then filtered, and imbibed by the patient after the addition of celery. Other drinks were prepared from linseed; fine wheat cooked in water and served chilled; Ethiopian cummin mixed with water and potter's clay with hair (*sic*) in it is recommended for all fevers; white wine derived from dry grapes and cut with water; egg whites beaten with water added; ripe, peeled cucumber in water; bitter vetch (*Vicia Ervilia*), thoroughly cooked in water, chilled and served with powdered cucumber and powdered vetch; Thasian wine, one part to twenty-five of water (!); a trefoil concoction; sweet apple cider (cut with water); and many more, some spiced with carthamus (*knikos, safflower*), celery, mint, coriander, or pennyroyal (*glechon, Mentha Pulegium*).

The violence of some of the treatments enjoined in *Diseases,* II and III, as well as in *Internal Medicine* (see below), led Littré to suppose that all three were Cnidian rather than Coan in spirit and origin.[4]

Several syndromes not directly discussed in either *Diseases* or *Internal Medicine,* are considered in the relatively brief compass of *Illnesses.* After a repetition of the statement which appears elsewhere that all diseases originate in phlegm and bile, the first-mentioned ailments are those which affect the head. Heat applied locally was prescribed and the need stressed to induce the removal of phlegm, which is apparently thought of as the causative agent, by sneezing. Dietary management included soup and water, wine being forbidden until the pain in the head ceased. The explanation for the latter is that a heated head draws wine to it, increasing pain and discomfort. For pain alternating with vertigo, bleeding was done of the nostrils or frontal vein. If the illness were prolonged, incisions were made in the patient's scalp, or else the veins were cauterised in a circle. Bad medicine as this may seem, an analogous procedure was proposed, according to Littré, in the year 1848, when it made its appearance in the *Bulletin de l'Académie de médicine!* This procedure was characterized by the ancient writer as the only one which gave hope of healing (chapter 2).

If the ears became involved, applications of heat and fomentations (steaming) were used, along with phlegmagogues, emetics or purgatives, a gargle for the throat if inflamed, and something to chew on (*diamassetoisi chresthai*) if the gums or undertongue were affected. The uvula might be engorged and cause choking: for this, if gargling failed to help, bleeding by leeches applied *to the back of the head* was approved, and if that failed, then the lancing of the uvula with a bistoury was done, in order to let the water out. As for the teeth, if a tooth caused pain, revealed caries, and was loose, removal of the offending tooth was thought necessary; however, if the tooth showed neither caries nor looseness, it had to be dried by burning; again, something to chew might be helpful.

A snare was used to remove nasal polyps, which were believed also to be caused by phlegm.

Chapter 8 is the source of the definition of the important term "crisis": it is defined as the time "when diseases increase, weaken, change into a different disease, or terminate."

Winter fevers, whatever their cause, had to be guarded against lest they become acute disease; a liquid diet was enjoined, with rest, and the reduction of weight, as well as keeping the bowels open (chapter 12). The utmost precaution and the most careful treatment are demanded of the physician in acute diseases.

Summer fevers seemed to require more versatile treatment, but the treatment was chiefly dietary (soups and drinks), and purgative at both ends of the alimentary tract.

A "summer gastritis" also required purgation, including an emetic made of honey-and-water (*melikreton*) and vinegar to be drunk tepid, but bathing in warm water and fomentations for relief of pain were also prescribed. Pain was also treated by the use of drugs (the description of which was to be sought in a handbook of chemotherapy called *Pharmakitis,* which has not survived, most unfortunately). Apparently, when pain persisted, nourishment was withheld (chapter 5).

Afebrile malaise with pain called for hot baths and fomentations —to disperse the concentrations of bile (chapter 16).

Tertian and quartan (malarial) fevers are said to predominate chiefly in summer, though there may be outbreaks in winter, too. Treatment was of course adapted to the various alternations of days on which the febrile paroxysms occurred or recurred, and consisted of evacuations, medications (again the handbook, *Pharmakitis,* is referred to) to reduce fever; when the fever attacks, the patient is kept on a liquid diet (indicating a grasp of the need for adequate hydration); on the intervening days, laxative foods (solids) could be consumed. Tertian fever is considered not too serious provided that it is properly treated, to prevent its becoming a quartan fever and of lengthy duration (that each type of fever depended on invasion by one or more independent groups of parasites could not then have been known). Quartan fevers were to be treated pretty much like tertians, except that purgatives, including emetics, were more liberally employed, along with hot baths; both fevers arise from bile and phlegm.

It should be noted that, if *Diseases, Illnesses,* and *Internal Medicine* are products of the Cnidian school rather than the Coan school of medicine, so must *Pharmakitis* (often called *Pharmaka*), to which there are in Illnesses seven separate references, be Cnidian. Where the same diseases are discussed, there is commonly some variation noticeable in the usually minor aspects of treatment or the details thereof.

Hypertrophy of the spleen called for a regime of purgations, hellebore emetics, dehydration generally insofar as adjustment of foods and drinks could achieve this, and a great deal of exercise, including walks (*peripatoi*); in addition to these, there were frequent bleedings of the splenitic vein of the arm, diuretics, cholagogues, cauterization should there be suppuration, and the last mentioned may be the ultimate means of cure (chapter 20).

Dysentery, with abdominal pains and griping in the intestines, and loss of bile, phlegm, and calcined blood, required purgation of the head, phlegmagogic emetics, washing the gut out with boiled milk, cathartics, and hot soaks for pain, with a largely liquid diet detailed in *Pharmakitis.* If the case was complicated by a kind of ulcerative colitis, it was hopeless (chapter 23).

The same treatment as the foregoing was also prescribed for lientery (defined as the "passage of food without digestion into the stools"): pain is absent but there is progressive wasting of the body. Its cause is a phlegmatic flux (chapter 24).

Chronic diarrhea required "drying" of the upper body with hellebore and purging the head. The gut was washed with boiled milk. Diet was regulated to insure dehydration. Dysentery, lientery, and diarrhea were considered closely related and produced by the same causes (chapter 25).

The next ailment, tenesmus (*teinesmos,* straining at stool or ineffectual desire to void bowel or bladder) is grouped with the preceding for obvious reasons, but not considered serious or of long duration (chapter 26).

Cholera is attributed to excess in consumption of wine or (rich?) food (*euochie*)—nowadays ascribed to a specific germ, *Spirillum Cholerae asiaticae*—but the disease entity seems to be the same, called for a very restricted liquid diet of sweet wine or pressed grapes (*stemphyla glykea*), with purgation and emetics, as well as pain medication (set forth in *Pharmakitis*), and hot baths (chapter 27).

Strangury (extremely painful, stillicidous urination was thought to be of many different forms. The intent of treatment was to increase the quantity of urine by dietary means, and to control the pains of micturition by diuretic medications as listed in *Pharmakitis*. The cause was ascribed to phlegm, and the disease was not considered fatal, but much more prevalent and of lengthier duration in the young (chapter 28).

Hip disease (coxalgia and possibly sciatica) was treated by emollients locally, baths, fomentations, hot application, purgatives, and boiled asses' milk. (Again, *Pharmakitis* is referred to as the source of pain medications.) When all else failed to relieve the pain, cauterization was done with raw flax (*omolinon*). The ailment was long and painful but not fatal (chapter 29).

The discussion of arthritis is remarkable for the statement that it is more apt to effect the *young* than the old, and possible also for the observation that both pain and site of pain are repeatedly changing. The treatment given is mostly palliative, but there is also emphasis on keeping the bowels open and feeding the patient with whey or asses' milk. The cause is bile and phlegm which become fixed in the joints. The disease is said to be acute and of short duration (chapter 30).

Podagra was recognized as the most painful and violent of joint diseases, as well as the most tenacious of its victim. It is called a defect of the blood caused by bile and phlegm. Treatment was the same as for arthritis; but cauterization of veins in the big toes was resorted to if the pain settled there (chapter 31).

It is interesting that the administration of cholagogues and phlegmagogues is said to be more dangerous and productive of complaints against the persons who administer them (the writer here uses the term *therapeuontes,* literally, "attendants," for which Littré uses the French *médecins,* or physicians), than that of any other food, beverage, or medication (chapter 33).

Tumors were treated with cataplasms (i.e., plasters or "poultices"), and internal purgations, but they might be incised to permit the liquid contents to escape, unless this happened spontaneously; the resulting opening was treated like a wound (chapter 34).

Dermatalogical conditions are flatly called deformities (*aischos*) rather than diseases! The list of such deformities includes leprosy, prurigo, scabies (psoriasis?), lichen, alopecia, scrofula, swollen glands (*phygethla*), carbuncles, and boils (chapter 35).

In general, medications were chosen by their appropriateness to the constitution of the patient: cholagogues for the bilious, phlegmagogues for the phlegmatic, for melancolics, black bile purges, etc. (chapter 36); so the initial examination was designed to determine this typology, among other matters (chapter 37).

Elaborate cataplasms or plasters, purgatives, and liquid diets were prescribed for wound cases (chapter 38). Dirty wounds were distinguished from clean (at least in a certain sense or degree), and putrifying wounds, also, required cleansing with acrid or pungent preparations, analogous to modern antiseptics or germicides; but if the purpose was the same, the theory of asepsis was of course lacking.

Patients whose condition contraindicated bathing were to be given an ointment of wine and warm olive oil, and rubbed every other day: the modern equivalent and the underlying rationale of this therapy are readily recognizable (chapter 42). Hot baths are mentioned in chapter 53 and their effects noted.

Illnesses concludes with a sort of handbook of observations, not on particular diseases and their management but on more general features of treatment of the ill (chapters 39–61). There is detailed emphasis on means used, by type, rather than on procedures. These include foods, drinks, the preparation of soups, diets for purged patients, or for various purposes, the use of medications, the preparation of solid food for different nutritive purposes, the choice of wines, and the nutritive properties of legumes, vegetables, fruits, and spices (e.g., onions, celery, coriander, ocimum, leeks, pomegranates), and many other items in the diet.

The opening sentence of *Illness* does suggest that the author may have intended the work as a sort of home medical reference (as Littré supposed), but the *content* of chapters 1-38 seems much too technical for direct use by a layman. The two halves in which the work readily divides itself make it much more likely that they were really intended for medical students. This is probably true for several other essays in the Hippocratic Collection.

Internal Diseases (*Peri ton entos pathon*) is one of the longest essays in the Collection, after works like *Epidemics, Coan Prognoses, Joints, Diseases,* and *Regimen,* with about sixty-five pages of text. It contains a considerable amount of discussion of matters discussed in *Diseases,* II, which I shall omit. There is evident, also, the "multiplication of disease entities," as Edelstein called it, a refinement of disease classification for which the Cnidian school was famous and, to some, notorious.[5] For example, there is not one phthisis but several, not one lung inflammation but many, not one renal disease but four, not one hydropsy but three, plus general hydropsy, three hepatitises, five diseases of the spleen, four icteruses, five tetanuses including opisthotonus, and so on.

For a kidney ailment the author recommends first a steam bath of the whole body, then as a purgative the juice or even the root of scammony (*Convolvulus scammonia*); another purgative the following day, a drink based on white chickpeas (*erebinthos,* or *Cicer arietinum*), touched up with salt just before it was drunk; for pain, sponging with hot water or application of heat topically. If there was swelling, *surgery of the kidney* was directed to evacuate the pus, and removal of stones by the use of diuretics. He explicitly states that in this variety of the illness, surgery is the only procedure which affords a chance of recovery. Nephrotomy was not again to be practiced with any such degree of confidence until the nineteenth century.[6] Another variety of kidney ailment, termed *phthisie rénale* by Littré, was also eligible for surgical intervention (chapter 15), but the hazards are very evident, including involvement of the other kidney.

A rheumatoid disease with coxalgia was treated, among several adjustments of diet and even cauterization by mushrooms (*sic*), by having the patient imbibe Mendaean wine until the nose bled (*methyskestho achris an haimorrhagese kata tas rhinas*), which it was permitted to do for three days (chapter 18).

The treatment for a hydropsy with symptoms of dry cough, roughness in the throat, chills, fever, orthopnoea, moderate swelling of the body, engorgement of tissues of the feet (local edema), and retraction of the nails, was as follows: hot bath, then shaking by the shoulders to determine by auscultation which side revealed the most "fluctuation," (now called [Hippocratic] succussion), as a preliminary to selecting a site for trepanation done on the third rib to evacuate the accumulated water, and which Littré likened to a recently invented treatment for thoracic paracentesis. In addition to the usual dietary prescription, baths, and purgatives, if edema subsequently developed in the genitals and thighs, scarification by numerous punctures in the affected areas was strongly recommended (the physician is told to act boldly, *tharseon*).

Hot packs were used to ameliorate the pain of hepatitis. When the pain subsided, honey-and-water (*melikreton*) or an astringent sweet white wine, and the same soups recommended for cases of pleurisy, were offered the patient. Also, the yolk of a cooked hen's egg, mixed with the juice of *strychnon* (*Solanum dulcamara*) and the highly regarded *melikreton*. He could also have goat's milk, again with honey (one third) in the morning. As emetic was prescribed if the patient showed signs of suffocation (choking, *pnigma*). There were many grain and meat dishes available to the patient: meats if boiled, as well as boiled fish (dogfish—a kind of small shark; torpedo—the electric ray; and skate—small-sized). Ambulation was permitted but on a restricted basis until the patient was out of danger (chapter 27).

Hellebore was used for splenitis; and evacuation of the bowels by administering *kokkos Knidios* (a berry of the shrub *kneoron, Daphne Gnidium*). A great variety of nutriments were thought to be suitable for such a patient. The medicamentarium (to secure progressive reduction of the spleen) included asphodel, leaves of oak-mistletoe (*Hozanthus europaeus*), fenugreek (called *aigokeras* or *telis* (*Trigonella foenum-graecum*), chaste-tree (*Vitex Agnus-castus*), mountain-rue, or root of didymaeum (salep, *Orchis papilionacea*). If the patient was able, a brisk program of exercise was set down: sawing wood (for thirty days), daytime walks, late to

bed and early to rise. Ten large eschars incised by cautery, again
with mushrooms (!), were made into the spleen at the most swollen
(chapter 30). Splenitic patients were not to indulge in coitus (chapter 32) or excessive imbibition of wine.

Hellebore was also prescribed for icterus (jaundice). The patient
might also have blister-beetles (*Cantharis vesicatoria*), with wings
and head removed, mixed with white wine and a little honey *ter*
or *quater in diem* (three or four times a day); and baths. Patients
with this type of icterus are unable to tolerate any bodily coverings
because of itching (*knesmos*), and their weakness is so great that
they cannot support their own weight sufficiently to walk (chapter
36). A third type of icterus or jaundice is called "epidemic" (*epid-
emios*) "because it strikes at every time of year" (*dioti pasan horen
epilambanei;* prompt treatment is indicated, first by bleeding the
veins of the arms at the elbow, and following with a steam bath,
and squirting cucumber (*Ecballium Elaterium*); on the third day,
asses' milk was given to purge the bowels, and a concoction prepared from the thick knee plover (*Charadrius oedicnemus*), finely
divided in white wine (chapter 37). A less severe case (with different etiology?) could have mainly dietary treatment and a special
gargle, in addition to the usual icteral treatment (medication, vapor
baths).

A malady called typhus (*typhos*) and associated in its onset with
the late summer rising of the Dogstar called for the interdiction of
all bathing, and anointing with warmed wine and olive oil, soft
diet, astringent black or white wine cut with water, cold water compresses to relieve fever (removed at the first sign of chilling), and
remedies indicated for pleurisy; the disease is difficult to manage and
few escape with their life (chapter 39).

Another so-called typhus (but termed acute rheumatoid arthritis
by Littré) marked by swellings particularly in the joints was treated
with heat topically, vapor baths, hellebore, whey from goat's milk,
bloodletting with a leech or cupping instrument which resembled the
bottle-gourd or cucumber, but only if the swelling was in the knees,
and then the means of puncture was a triangular needle (*akis
trigonos*): diet and ambulation are prescribed; the disease is more
often fatal than not (chapter 41).

There is a remarkable description of a so-called typhus characterized by striking symptoms: dehydration, accompanied by damp
skin, yellow complexion, "transparency"—"like a bladder full of

urine"—no edema, but pronounced wasting especially noticeable at the clavicles and the face, and sunken eyes; with intervals of blinking; the patient chases flies from his coverlet; hunger is marked; the smell of an extinguished lamp is very pleasant to him; pollutions are frequent, and he may even lose semen while walking. Purgations and a soft diet were employed, with whey, or cow's miik or goat's milk (asses' milk being used as a purgative, too). The disease is one of the most lasting mentioned in the Collection: two to twenty years, and confined to those over twenty years of age. This stubborn and difficult ailment was termed *maladie nerveuse by Littré* (chapter 43), who thought that it merited modern attention.[7]

Wild cucumber leaves mixed with honey, salt, olive oil, and beet juice was prescribed for an *eileos haimatites* or sanguinary ileus marked by foul breath, detachment of the gums from the teeth, and nosebleeds; the patient may also suffer from ulcerations of the legs, "black" complexion, and wasting of the flesh as well as great weakness. He was also to drink cow's milk for forty days, with a one-third mixture of *melikreton,* the much esteemed honey-and-water (chapter 46).

The finger was used as now to test the visual response of the patient; the use is recorded in the description of a very complex syndrome of disease which is merely called "thick" (without definition or explanation of the term chosen): the patient failed to blink (the pupils were dilated and the patient was in fact blind, or nearly so). The many other symptoms encountered in such a patient included swollen liver, cephalalgia, especially at the temples, reduced sense of hearing, chills and fever, and delirium when the liver obtrudes upon the diaphragmatic space. The patient picks at the coverlets, thinking their threads are lice; in his delirium he thinks he sees snakes, reptiles, monsters, and soldiers fighting; he may act as if he were in battle, too, his sleep intermittent and apparently interrupted by nightmares (*enhypnia phobera*); and his feet are constantly cold. It is said that the same set of symptoms was recorded in the attack of madness suffered by Charles VI of France (also called the Mad or Well Beloved; he died in 1422). Black hellebore was prescribed in a sweet wine, and a wash of Egyptian nitre with honey and beet juice, or asses' milk. The prognosis improved if the patient managed to survive the first seven days (chapter 48).

A kind of anaphylactic shock is mentioned in a disease syndrome

involving sudden collapse of the patient on smelling dust after a
shower of rain; the possibility of some *allergy* being involved is
increased by the statement that the disease begins with swelling of
the facial tissues, followed by swelling in the abdomen. The disease
lasts generally six years (chapter 50).

The last chapters of *Internal Medicine* concern a coxalgia treated
with cauterization (one of the lengthiest chapters is devoted to this
sickness), four varieties of *tetanos,* and a brief paragraph on opisthotonus.

There are, of course, a great many other works in the Hippocratic corpus from which a complete survey of Therapeutics must
be drawn, essays like those dealing with the treatment of ulcers,
head injuries, and problems of an orthopedic, gynecological, or
pediatric nature, as well as a group of works devoted to the theory
of "crises" or critical days so important in the medicine of the Hippocratics. All should be considered in order to have a complete
picture—insofar as the manuscript tradition has preserved it for
us—of Hippocratic medicine. I hope to return to a consideration of
several of these works at a later time.

Two points in particular stand out with regard to the therapeutics surveyed in the foregoing: (1) the great emphasis on largely
conservative means of treatment, particularly purgations, baths, diet
therapy, rest, and exercise; and (2) the willingness and even readiness to perform surgical procedures, though these are limited in
number and type. It may also be said that certain preoccupations
of the Hippocratic writers concerned matters now usually left in
their detailed pursuit or control to the "other" members of the medical team, to physiotherapists, to dietitians, to nurses, and even to
subprofessionals. There is also a notion of "cleanliness" in treatment or care of the patient, but lacking knowledge of bacteria and
germ theory there is, of course, no awareness of the need for asepsis, and relatively little evidence of concern for contagion or exposure to infection. Ignorance of such matters may in fact have made
practitioners braver. And some of them, in their customary mode of
traveling from one state or island to another, were undoubtedly on
more than one occasion, carriers of the diseases to which they unin-
hibitedly and unsuspectingly exposed themselves. Unlike the Egyptian school of medical practitioners, the Hippocratics seem seldom
to have refused treatment, even on the grounds of incurability of
the disease: they seem almost always to have felt that *something*

could be done at least to ease human suffering. In addition, we have a veritable wealth of evidence that the Hippocratics were excellent observers, remarkable diagnosticians within the limits of their science and the modest technology available to them, inventive and imaginative in the therapeutic situation, as well as both sympathetic and objective to a degree, and both of these things simultaneously, with superb powers of expression, as they went about recording the multiplicity of phenomena presented to their attention. Their combined achievements marked the highwater of medical theory and practice in antiquity which the subsequent history of the Hellenistic period failed to promote or even support and within a century of the assumed death of Hippocrates (c.370 B.C., traditionally) the great era of *Forschung,* of inquiry and investigation, appears to have ended or to have fallen to less worthy successors, with some notable exceptions, but very few in number. The most salient achievement of these successors was to preserve the Hippocratic tradition by collecting the writings that tradition had produced, by codifying and canonizing it, and by the commentaries they wrote on this or that work in the Collection; but it was no longer the living, growing thing that it had been. Yet, aside from its influence on Arabic medicine, it had no rival in prestige in Western Europe over the fifteen centuries which followed.[8]

CHAPTER 6

Environmental Medicine and the Laosphere

> . . . *the Hippocratic Corpus has a significant message for almost every thinking person concerned with man in health and in disease.*
>
> —René Dubos.

> The seasons, the land, and the waters . . . Hippocrates, *Airs, Waters, Places,* ch. XXIV.

I cannot better begin this final chapter on the Hippocratic Collection than with the quotation above from the distinguished scientist, René Dubos, who describes himself as "a microbiologist not trained in medicine" (in the "Preface" to his *Man Adapting,* p. xxi), not only because his scientific credentials are impeccable and thereby lend weight to his appreciation of the Hippocratic doctrines, but also because that same appreciation is perhaps the most conspicuous among moderns. It is also remarkable that such appreciation should finally come, not from a man of medicine as such, but from a scientist shaped by the evolving discipline of microbiology, which has already achieved so much in the understanding of the organism. The essential thing is that the study of the Hippocratics has still something of value which the lapse of time and successive advances in knowledge do not erode or render obsolete.[1]

Environmental medicine, as yet a hope for the future, may be the latest child of the thinking which produced both genetics and ecology in the last years of the nineteenth century, both of which were prepared for by the natural selection of Darwin (1859) and the "oecology" of Ernst Haeckel (1869). The study of ecosystems has received the greatest stimulus, however, from successive disasters in the environment initiated by man, who is not only the adapter to and of his environment, but also its destroyer. From *Homo dirutor,* Man the Destroyer, neither the landscape, nor the atmosphere, neither fauna or flora, has been safe.[2] The race to determine his own survival or extinction has already begun. It seems only sensible to be pessimistic about the outcome. But the healing art, *techne ietrike,* is nothing if not optimistic. It therefore is only sensible to look to environmental studies, of which such a medicine may be the long delayed capstone, for a resolution of the crisis in all its awesome imminence.

Wherever the environment is significantly altered or affected by the presence of man, wherever it is controlled or conditioned by his acts, wherever his relationship to the environment determines a critical or crucial factor (and this is practically wherever man is or goes, but especially when his is the felt presence of great numbers), we have a man-adapted-environment which for convenience I shall call the *laosphere* (from the Greek words, *laos,* meaning "people," or "mankind," and *sphaira,* meaning "ball," "globe," or "sphere"), which is also less clumsy than the term "anthroposphere," to which objection has been made, for example, by the naturalist Marston Bates in a recent lecture. Now the concept of environment which we find in *Airs, Waters, Places* is understandably one in which man's role in the ecosystem is far more passive than controlling, as we know it so often to be today, but we cannot demand a fuller awareness of the essential interdependence of man and his environment than that revealed by the author of the essay we are considering. It stands upon its own merits, whether or not we think it justifiable to look upon its author as the founder of bioclimatology, meteorology, and hydrotherapy," in the words of Eugene Phocas, which may indeed be more metaphor than matter, after all, more admiration than sophistication.[3]

The three factors which impinge most on man are those which make up the essay title (in Greek, *Peri aeron, hydaton, topon*): Climate, Water Supply, Topography, and of these Climate predominates.

In what follows, I have, for convenience, written of *Airs, Waters, Places* (AWP) as a work of single and unique authorship, though this is yet contestable, and agreement has not been reached. The question of sole or double authorship turns upon the apparent switch in topic, from the first half (consisting of chapters 1–11) dealing with the effects of climate and locale on health, to the second (chapters 12–24), which is mainly concerned with effects of climate on character; hence the supposition by some of either two authors or at least two separate works. (Oddly, *both* views seem to be entertained almost simultaneously—only four pages apart from each other—by Robert Joly in whose *Niveau de la science hippocratique* I find these two statements: 1 *"Airs, Waters, Places* seems to us a single work, in spite of various German theories which admit to two separate works and even at times to two authors"; and 2 "This rather extraordinary divergence"—apparent contradictions in the application of the humoral theory"—and which is far from being the only one—excluded in our view the unity of authorship".[4]

The basis of inclusion of the author's topics in a work designed for the perusal of physicians and medical students is contained in the flat statements with which the introductory portion of *AWP* begins and ends: first, whoever wishes to investigate medicine properly, must consider the annual seasons and the effects of each, as well as the winds, and the waters in their variance from one place to another; and, second, astronomy, far from having a minor effect on medicine, contributes considerably to it, since both diseases and the organs of digestion change right along with the changes in the seasons.

That the composition of *AWP* was inspired partly by the demands of an often peripatetic practice, marked by frequent departures and arrivals from one locale to another is obvious from the repeated statement that knowledge of the seasonal sort discussed in the essay was essential in order to remove the handicap which the practitioner's sojourn in unfamiliar places would otherwise expose him to. He will instead enjoy the advantage of knowing what to expect (an argument common to so much of the Hippocratic Collection). The injunction to the practitioner is *proginoskein tous kairous* ("to know-in-advance the critical opportunities and their advantages," chapter 2, end).

The demonstration of the author's thesis of the importance of "meteorological" information to the physician begins with the description of a "typical" locale, one in which the *polis* or city in its human and politico-physical configuration is exposed to hot winds, "between the winter rising and setting of the sun," sheltered against the north winds, where the waters are abundant, salty (brackish?), close to the surface, hot in summer, and cold in winter (chapter 3).

The natives of such a region have humid heads full of phlegm which affects their digestive organs for the worse from the preval-

ence of phlegmatous catarrhs. Most of the denizens tend to flabbiness and they are not good at either eating or drinking, the latter
partly because persons with weak heads suffer more from the hang-
overs consequent on excessive drinking. Diseases peculiar to the
region include infertility among women (the result of disease processes), high incidence of abortion, infantile convulsions, asthma,
and epilepsy (all three characterized as diseases to which children
in particular are subject), while the adult males are prone to dysentery, diarrhea, ague (now defined as a malarial fever with chill, fever,
and sweating—from the French word for acute: *aigu*), chronic
wintertime fever, *epinyctides* (pustules most painful during the
night), and hemorrhoids. Rarely encountered in the region are
pleurisy, pneumonia, *causos* (high fever), and acute illnesses generally, though the inhabitants are liable of course to epidemic diseases as well as those above mentioned which are of an endemic
nature. Men over fifty may be paralyzed by catarrhs whose source
is in the brain if they are suddenly exposed to sun on their heads
or sudden chills.

The contrary of the above picture is a city so placed as to face
cold winds which prevail from the time between the summer setting
and rising of the sun, though sheltered from the southerly wind
(*Notos*) and the hot winds of the south and southwest. The
waters here are usually dense (*sklera*) and cold. Natives of this
region are muscular and lean, and tend to be constipated in the
lower digestive tract but loose in the upper portion. They are
choleric (bilious) rather than phlegmatic, with hard, healthy heads,
and a tendency to lesion or rupture of tissues (of lungs?). Their endemic diseases are pleurisy, abscesses, acute illnesses, and, in men
under thirty, violent nosebleeds in summer. The proneness to lesion
(*rhegmatias*) mentioned above is ascribed to their bodily dryness
(*xerotes*) and the coldness of the water they drink. Consequently,
they are heavy eaters and light drinkers. Eventually (*dia chronou*)
they may develop ophthalmias which result in ocular ruptures
(*rhegnysthai ta ommata*). Epilepsy is rare but violent when it does
occur. Their longevity is greater than that of other men, presumably
in other regions (there is some ambiguity in the phraseology used
in the text). Many of the women experience barrenness, from the
waters, which are dense, difficult to digest (*ateramna*), and cold.
Their menses are unhealthy, thin, and poor in quality. For them
childbirth is difficult, but abortion is uncommon. The waters again

make it impossible to breastfeed their infants. Phthisis (a wasting disease) often develops after parturition from the violence of the latter with its ensuing ruptures and strains. The male young are dropsical in the testes when young, but the condition disappears with increasing age. Puberty in such a city comes late (chapter 4).

The best situation for a city is to face the risings of the sun, since the extremes of heat and cold are more moderate. Also, the waters in such a situation must be bright, clean-smelling, soft, and very pleasant, a result of the beneficent influence of the rays of the rising sun. The natives are apt to have good, clear complexions and they flourish like flowers. By comparison with those exposed to the north, these people are clear-voiced with better temperament and intelligence. The city so situated is like spring among the seasons. Though subject to similar ailments affecting others in a south exposure, these sicknesses are among them fewer and less violent. Conception occurs very readily among the women and they deliver easily (chapter 5). An Eden or a Shangri-La!

The worst location for a city is to face the setting of the sun, while sheltered from east winds and both hot winds and cold northerlies sweep over them. In such a location, the waters lack limpidity, owing to the morning mist which dissolves in them, the sun failing to break through until midday and so unable to clean them with its rays. In summer cold breezes blow in the morning and dews fall; but the advancing sun scorches the inhabitants as it moves to its setting, who as a result tend to be sickly and prone to all the ailments. Their voices are apt to be deep and hoarse because of the air which is usually unclean and unhealthy. The prevailing winds are extremely wet, so the climate generally resembles autumn in view of the extremes of temperature changes during a single day (chapter 6).

Chapters 7–9 are devoted to waters and their effects on health. These effects are characterized generally as extremely important (*pleiston gar meros symballetai es ten hygieien*).

Marshy, stagnant waters are in summer hot, thick, and smelly, poor in color, unhealthy, and bilious; in winter they are icy, cold, and turbid as a result of the snows and freezing to which they are subject, and so tend to cause production of phlegm and hoarseness in the throat. Such waters cause stiff, enlarged spleens in those who drink of them. They develop hard, thin, hot stomachs, with loss of flesh in the shoulders, collarbone area and the face (ascribed to the flesh in these parts "dissolving" to feed the spleen). A further consequence is that they eat and drink heavily (contradicting the statement in chapter 4 that one cannot be both a heavy eater and drinker). Their digestive tracts are extremely dry and hot, with the result that they require stronger medications, year around. Dropsy is common and generally fatal. Summer brings epidemics of dysentery, diarrhea, and lasting quartan fever, with secondary dropsy resulting in death. Winters cause pneumonias in the young and ailments accompanied by delirium, while older persons contract *causos* (bilious remittent fever). The women have edemas and leucophlegmasias (defised as a type of dropsy or *anasarca*—"a generalized infiltration of edema fluid into subcutaneous connective tissue"). In addition, they have difficulty in conceiving and in delivery. Infants are large and swollen; as they are nursed they lose weight and have much pain. The postpartum discharge of females is poor. Hernias are common in children, while adult males suffer varicosities and tumors (or, suppurating sores) on their legs and generally they age before their time. The women, who tend to dropsy, are prone to pseudocyesis (false pregnancy).

Rocky springs also have waters almost as bad as the foregoing. Likewise, earth (ground) waters which are hot, or mineral-bearing are bad; for example, those with deposits of iron, copper, silver, gold, sulphur, alum, bitumen, or soda. Such waters are hard and cause heating and constipation.

The healthiest waters flow from high places and earthy hills. They are characterized by being sweet and clear; they will not take much wine. They are also warm in winter, cool in summer, since they come from the deepest springs. The very best flow toward the summer rising of the sun, just as the very worst face south or between the winter rising and setting, especially if the winds are in the south.

A person in good health can drink any kind of water; not so the person who is ill or whose constitution predispose them to certain risks. Salt water is not laxative as most ignorant people suppose; rather, it is constipating (chapter 7).

Rain water is the lightest, sweetest, finest, and most limpid. This results from the action of the sun which draws to the surface the finest and lightest water, while heavier solids sink, as is the case with salt. The sun so affects not only pools of water but also the sea and anything containing moisture, even human bodies, which give up their perspiration to the sun wherever they are exposed to it. For the same reason, rain water is more apt to turn foul quicker than other waters and develop a bad odor. In part, the characteristics of rain water are due to their source in the clouds aloft and the buffeting they receive from the winds. Such waters ought to be boiled to rid them of foulness and bad odor and to prevent their becoming a source of soreness, coughing, and hoarseness.

Snow water and ice water are always bad. Once water freezes, it never regains its original character, but loses its best part, the turbid and heavy portions remaining. A simple test in winter-time will demonstrate that the lightest portion, which is also the best, evaporates. So, no matter what the purpose intended, such waters are the worst (chapter 8).

Drinking many different waters, or waters from large rivers to which others are tributary, or from lakes fed by all sorts of streams, or waters originating at a considerable distance, is apt to cause kidney stones, kidney disease, strangury, sciatica, and hernias, owing to the sediments they bear. There follows a description and explanation of how urination is affected by waters (and other liquids such as milk and wine). The writer notes that females suffer from kidney stones less than males do and attributes this to the fact that their urethra is short and wide, so that they micturate more easily. He also notes that they do less rubbing of their genitals than males do and do not handle the urethra owing to its direct opening into the genitalia. They also drink more than boys do (chapter 9).

Chapters 10–11, which conclude the first half of *AWP,* as previously mentioned, list in detail the signs which seasons give at their inception and the types of ailments which may therefore be anticipated. That this is a prescientific but persistent "folk" medicine rather typical of laymen today will be readily recognized. Yet it is only right to say that an informal practice of weather-and-disease prognostication exists because of the gap in medical science, which folk medicine never hesitates to fill, since it responds and corresponds so quickly to every human need, far outstripping the endeavors of the patient few to set matters on a rational footing. This aspect of medical practice, like environmental medicine generally, of which it is the smaller part, is an area of great growth for the future. In the ancient writer, as we would expect from other parts of the Hippocratic Collection, the emphasis on the significance of sudden or violent changes in the weather is very strong. Few of the details, interesting though they may be, need detain us here, with the exceptions noted in the immediately following:

Cautery or surgery of the bowels is contraindicated when very violent changes in the seasons have occurred. Specifically, the most violent seasonal changes, and therefore the most dangerous, are the solstices (especially in summer) and the equinoxes (especially in autumn). Also to be guarded against are the sidereal risings, particularly those of the Dog Star, and Arcturus, but also the setting of the Pleiads: these are the times when diseases come to their crisis.

Part two of *AWP* is a unique application by extension of environmental notions of medicine to ethnic or racial and cultural distinctions which are conceived of as originating in differences in climate and environment. It is impossible now to say how much the author of *AWP* was influenced by popular ideas of his own day, how much by the more learned of his contemporaries and predecessors, and again to determine how much, if any direct, influence his essay has had since its composition. Yet much of it, good or bad, has become the currency of the vulgar, commonplace and pseudo-scientific, anthropological, and a rich vein of injurious prejudice. Nowhere else, not even in Herodotus, a contemporary of Hippocrates, though older than the latter by some twenty years, is the East-West thought axis more sharply defined in Greek or Latin literature. It must be kept in mind, however, that in the contrastive juxtapositions brought about by the author of *AWP,* the two terms used are "Asia" and "Europe." Unfortunately missing is a section on Africa, except for the final sentence which refers to Egyptians and Libyans. But the Asia of most ancients extends merely to the confines of what we call Asia Minor, and the existence of Hindus, let alone Chinese, is not even hinted; so we should think of the Middle East plus some portion of the hinterlands beyond it whenever we read in *AWP* a reference to Asia.

The dividing point between the two land masses is for the author Lake Maeotis, according to the ancient appellation, but now called the Sea of Azov, the shallow northern bay of the Black Sea, rather than, as we should expect, the Bosporus or Hellespont (Dardanelles), at the mouth of the Black Sea.

Apart from the now lost references to Egyptians and Libyans, the few peoples, races, or nations (the Greek term for all three is *ethne*) mentioned by name in Chapters 12–24 of *AWP* include the following: the Macrocephaloi or "Longheads" (identified as a Crimean people by a German physician named H. Rathke, who served there in 1843 or earlier, and whose memoir, which appeared in the *Archiv für Anatomie, Physiologie, u.s.w.,* that year, is cited by *Littré,* Vol. IV, pp. xi–xii); Phasians (dwellers on the Phasis River, famed in mythology for its connection with the Argonauts and the Colchian witch-princess Medea); Hellenes, of course; Scythian Sauromatae or Sarmatians (ancestors of the Slavic peoples of Russia and Poland); and lastly, the Nomadic Scythians, a subgroup of the former. The author specifically excludes from his discussion peoples very similar or closely related to these, justifiably from his point of view, which is to emphasize the distinctions he makes by contrasting disparate groups of peoples.

The author's contention is that the "races" of Europe and Asia (Minor) differ in all respects including their "outward appearance," for which the term used is *morphe* (translated by Jones as "physique"). But the difference between the two land masses is a pervasive one, involving the natures of all the things produced by the land as well as human beings. In Asia Minor everything develops to greater beauty and size by far, the land is more cultivated, and its inhabitants milder and better tempered in their character. The reason for this is the blending of the seasons (*kresis ton horeon*) which in turn is the consequence of its situation eastward between the sun's (seasonal) risings, and its being further than Europe from cold weather. Development and cultivation (*auxesis* and *hemerotes*) of everything is favored most of all by the absence of any single violently dominating factor and when instead there prevails in everything a "balance of constituent ingredients" (*isomoirie*). (The notion is quite the analogue of purely medical theories, including the humoral: equability of climate leads directly to equability of growth, individuation, and temperament; balance is everything, the highest and most controlling of important factors.)

Which is not to say that Asia Minor is everywhere and in all its characteristics the same, since differences do occur, but the area taken as a whole, with its "middleness" between extremes of temperatures, exhibits unusual fertility, is heavily wooded, and enjoys remarkably mild weather, while its waters whether from springs or rains are excellent. The land is protected therefore from burning heat and droughts and insufficiency of water just as it is untroubled by cold, and the wet and damp of inordinate rainfall and snows.

These excellences of climate bestow their benefactions, we are told, on the produce of the earth, whether from the domestic crops planted by men or from the plenteousness of earth's own un-assisted bounty, so much so that wild land is readily adapted to agriculture and growths of nature are readily adapted to domestic culture by simple transplantation. (It seems almost the description of an Edenic garden!) Domestic animals flourish in the region, re-producing their kind in large and healthy numbers.

Men themselves thrive in this climate, are very handsome in appearance, and very tall, with little distinction among them in appearance or size. (It is a common fact of either the obtuseness or naiveté of our perceptual apparatus that individuals in large groups appear to lose their distinguishing characteristics or to have none or few, though this is especially the case when the mass group is unfamiliar to us, in a way in which the Ionians and others de-scribed by the author of *AWP* could not have been.)

As with other regions described in the first half of *AWP,* in the whole complex of existing factors in climate, land, waters, and living things, the region under discussion is likened to a season of the year, and this region is like spring.

The very equability of the climate imposes certain *disadvantages,* however, both on the inhabitants who are natives of the region as well as on those who, by settlement therein from abroad, develop subsequently in the same psycho-physical directions: virility, the endurance of hardships and severe exertion, and a passionate spirited-ness cannot develop; instead pleasure-seeking must necessarily be dominant in satures so contrived (chapter 12).

It is at this point in the essay that we have lost the section which contained the description of the Egyptians and Libyans. As for the "Europeans," we must disentangle them to the extent that our use of the term is occasionally at variance with that of the ancient writer, for whom Scythians were Europeans, not Asiatics, and European too the mysterious Crimean Macrocephaloi or Longheads, and those obscure river dwellers, the Phasians.

The Macrocephaloi are a remarkable group and remarkable also are some of the writer's observations on them. He tells us that elongation of their heads was originally the result of deliberate practice and achieved in infants by the use of bandages and "suitable appliances," which gave an appearance that was highly valued and admired, but that eventually nature supplanted the practice very largely. So, in effect, he believed in the concept of inheritance of acquired characteristics and in fact argues, though confusedly, for such a concept by saying it is supported by the feature resemblance which children have to their parents, all such resemblances deriving from the "germ" or "seed" (*gonos*) which comes from every part of the body. He does note that longheadedness is less common in the population than it had been previously and ascribes this to increasing exogamy with other peoples among whom the practice no longer prevailed (chapter 14). We are not told, however, anything about the climate or topography of the region which the Macrocephaloi inhabited.

The lack of this information in the case of the Macrocephaloi is fully offset by the description of those who dwelt on the river Phasis. The region is marked by marshes, hot, wet, and heavily wooded, with heavy, even violent, rainfall. The natives occupied the marshes themselves by contriving dwellings of reed and wood which presumably were supported by pilings driven into the water. Consequently, they had little use for walking about the city and the center of trade, like other peoples, but sailed up and down in small boats fashioned from single logs (dugouts) since there were many canals.

The natives were forced to drink the hot, stagnant waters available, which were corrupted by the sun's rays and swollen by rainstorms. The river Phasis (mentioned by Virgil in the *Georgics,* iv. 367, as a far-off stream, part of whose waters were subterranean), 195 miles long and now named Rion, is described as the most stagnant of rivers with the most sluggish current. The produce of the region is vitiated by the excessive rainfall which prevents their developing and ripening fully. The land is wrapped in heavy mist (*eer polys*). Not surprisingly, the physical appearance of the Phasians is said to be different from other peoples! The Phasians are quite tall and overly heavyset so that neither joint nor vein is visible. Their complexion is yellowish as if from jaundice. Of all peoples, the Phasians have the deepest voices because the air they breathe is wet and dense instead of clear. Their physical constitution makes them rather unsuited to bodily exertion. The climate is marked as having only minor seasonal changes, normally without extreme heat or cold. The prevailing winds are wet except for one peculiar to the river valley, called the *kenchron,* which occasionally blows violent, harsh, and hot. The north wind seldom penetrates the region, and when it does it is weak and gentle (chapter 15).

But the dominant element of this half of *AWP* is its characterology, which is more psychological in its drift than directly medical in its orientation. The crucial factor to which the writer returns so often is that of change, change which underlies all the essences of development, of improvements, of detriments, of gains, of losses, of advance, progress, decline, and failure.

As changes are moderate in degree or few in number, so their influence is intermittent, slight, or negligible. But when they are abrupt, violent, totally opposite in character to what precedes them, and palpable, or numerous, then they produce the significant characteristics of which they are the analogues.

So it is the temperate climate and the restricted changes with their lack of extremes that account for the like character of the Asians as contrasted with the Europeans. The former display lack of spirit (*athymie*) and lack of virility or courage (*anandreie*). So, too, they are less warlike and more civilized in character than the Europeans, who are subject to much greater changes in climate and extremes of heat and cold. Shocks to the mind and violent change of the body, both of which tend to develop a temperament which is wild, headstrong, and passionate, are more typical of a changeable climate than one which is characterized by sameness. *The occurrence of changes in all things stimulates the thought processes of men and do not let them rest.* In addition to these factors, the impotence of the Asians may also be ascribed to their customs (*nomoi*)—as we might say, their "style of life."

It is apparent that in defending his thesis, the author has had to modify it and in a sense extend or enlarge it to admit of cases in a broadly generalizing fashion which betrays confusion of thought and only partial awareness of self-contradictions. The simplistic breadth of treatment only glosses over the fissures in his thinking. The cardinal issue however is whether these peoples govern themselves or not. Those who do govern themselves are the "most warlike of all men" (*machimotatoi eisi panton*)—yet these too are Asians! He cannot have it both ways simultaneously and yet insists on having it so as if a dogmatic utterance stubbornly insisted on would dissipate the contradiction. The real failure is that of approximating climatology and a theory of political institutions involving a very broad sort of characterology without supplying a connecting bridge between the two. The result of course is an unhappy failure to convince. Far from having glossed over the discrepancies, the author has left them in an emergent state. It is natural and "proper" surely to think of self-governing peoples as superior to those ruled by kings and despots, but it is certainly questionable that this sort of superiority necessarily involves vigor, virility, or martial spirit, among peoples who are better distinguished by the various degrees of consent and acquiescence in whatever each is urged or ordered to do. We can commend the quality of one response compared to the other and attach to it higher value from conviction out of a moral judgment; but as even the author of this interesting work admits, enslaved populations also demonstrate worthiness and valor (*chresta kai andreia*) when they are compelled by their master to serve in the army, endure hardship, and meet with death.

The most likely source of the contradictions in this passage is the strong feeling which survived the struggle of the Greeks (some of whom were self-governing) against the Persians, who vainly exploited against them the resources of what proved an unwieldy empire. The grain of truth is sunk in the germ of nationalistic fervor.

The physician who concerns himself with political issues may seem to have moved far beyond the sphere of medicine, and there is reason to be dubious or wary about medico-political practice, but it too has two sides, one bad and one good, and it would be naive to suppose that medical practice exists in a vacuum devoid of political notions, just as the philosophic contention may be advanced that medicine concerns the whole man in every corner of his being, the healthy man, and not just the sick man.

The ancient writers' laudable attempt to gather together detail of almost unlimited complexity and extended diffusion into a single comprehensive statement directed to significance and understanding inevitably runs aground on the twin paucities of insufficient evidence and insufficient depth of treatment. It remains a noble, not entirely misguided, but premature sketch or outline of a subject of perennial, consuming interest. Even with better, and presumably more sophisticated means of gathering and assessing evidence, the modern study of cultural differences seems still unprepared to deal definitively with the questions raised by one of the earliest of cultural anthropologists. When he does conclude the contrasts and comparisons of his discussion, he falls back upon climate and the changes in the seasons as determinants of superiority and inferiority among Asians themselves who differ from one another, having quickly lost sight of or abandoned the insights just offered on the effects of cultural diversity, which three sentences before were so compelling to him that he could make the observation that men *naturally* brave and spirited were liable to be corrupted by their customs or institutions (chapter 16).

It is remarkable that the author of *AWP* should select the Scythians as the one European people to describe extensively, as he does in most of the remaining chapters (17–22) of this essay. The Scythians in ancient times, and more particularly in the times of Hippocrates and Herodotus, were a people who lived in the area north and northeast of the Black Sea, between the Carpathian Mountains and the river Don. Their origin is not known, but their speech was what is called Indo-European. The chief ancient source for their history is the fourth book of the *Histories* of Herodotus, although, aside from the Hippocratic work discussed here, there are references to them in Strabo, Pliny the Elder, Ptolemy, Diodorus Siculus, and Justinus, not to mention occasional references in the poets, from Hesiod on down to late Roman times, when they are said to have ceased to exist as a distinct ethnic group.

According to the Hippocratic writer of *AWP*, the Scythian people, who dwelt about Lake Maeotis, were quite different from the other peoples (*diapheron ton ethneon ton allon*). They were called, he says, *Sauromatai* (possibly not the same as the group established in the same region at a subsequent date under the name of *Sarmatai* or Sarmatians, though the two are generally identified as being the same). (A Scythian people, called *Ashguzai,* in Hebrew *Ashkenaz,* joined with the Assyrians in the latter part of the seventh century B.C. in their attacks on the Cimmerians, the Medes, and the Egyptians; but the name *Ashkenaz* first appears in Genesis 10:3 as the name of the eldest son of Gomer, the son of Japheth who was the son of Noah.)[5]

According to the account given by Herodotus, it was the Scythians who originally penetrated Asia in pursuit of the Cimmerians and in so doing clashed with the Medes, whose empire they destroyed, and ruled in their place for a period of twenty-eight years before they were forcibly removed. There are certainly many difficulties in the Hippocratic account of the Scythians, but interpolation of the text is not one of them, in Edelstein's view (see his work on *AWP*, p.51, expanded from an original dissertation).

Remarkable too in this unique member of the Hippocratic corpus are the fabulous and even fantastic elements. It is not at all clear why the account given in chapter 17 should be devoted to the Sauromatian females, nor why the description of them should so closely tally with that of the legendary or mythical Amazons.

Herodotus does refer to a group of Scyths located just above the trading center of the Borysthenites (on the river Dnieper) and who are called Kallippidai as Greek Scyths (*Hellenes Skythai*). These may indeed have been the products of intermarriage, not merely Scyths who adopted Greek customs by trafficking with them, as Heinrich Stein contended in the last century in his 1877 edition of Herodotus (p. 21, note 3). Nowadays, in fact, it would not be too surprising if Greek and Scyth were found to be interconnected even in the second millennium B.C. The Herodotean passage is from chapter 17 of the fourth book of the *Histories*. Herodotus, of course, was not committed to Greek "purity," racially speaking. One story of Scythian origin which he recounts (and rejects, in favor of a more pragmatic version), apparently circulated among the Pontic Greeks who ascribed to Hercules' union with a maid-serpent in a cave the three children, including the eponymous Scythes, from whom the Scythian peoples stemmed. This was said to have occurred when Hercules was carrying off the cattle of Geryon (in a reversal of the geography of the canonical version of the Tenth Labor). Interestingly, Scythes, his youngest offsping by this strange union, founded the royal line of the Scythians because of his ability to draw Hercules' bow, which of course is a parallel to the much better known bow of Odysseus. Hercules, or Herakles, was engaged in his Ninth Labor to win the girdle of Hippolyta, the Amazon Queen, which brings us back to the women warriors of the Sauromatae as described in *AWP*.

The land of the Sauromatae was divided from that of the Royal Scyths by the Palus Maeotis. It is Herodotus and not the Hippocratic writer who gives us Scythic equivalents for the names of several Greek gods (for example, *Tabiti* for Hestia or Vesta, *Papaios* for Zeus, *Api* for Earth, *Goitosyros* for Apollo, *Argimpasa* for the Heavenly Aphrodite, and *Thagimasadas* for Poseidon or Neptune; see Book IV, chapter 59).

It is also Herodotus who tells us that the Amazons formed

alliances with the Scythians, each out of admiration for the warlike qualities of the other, which made them want to have offspring by each other (*Persian Wars,* iv. 110–117), but the Hippocratic writer does not mention this mixed origin of the Sauromatae, nor does he use the name "Amazon" in speaking of their women, yet his description of them squares in essential details with that of Herodotus. The unmarried women (*parthenoi*) ride horseback, and while mounted use both bows and javelins against their enemies. They marry only after killing three enemies and performing customary sacred rites.   Unlike Herodotus, who uses the name of "Amazon" to designate these women but does not apply to the name the usual derivation of *a-mazos* ("breastless"), the Hippocratic writer, without using the name "Amazon," records soberly enough that the women have no right breast, since this part of the body is cauterized in infancy by the mother, the purpose being to pass the strength and mass of this area to the right shoulder and arm. None of this is necessarily impossible, but there remains the question of choice and purpose in including the Sauromatae: why these people, and why the omission of any description of their men, the physique of either sex, and the climate and topography of the region which they are said to inhabit? All of these points are brought into the discussion of the Scythian Nomads in the six chapters which follow.

The physical appearance of the Scythians, which sets them apart from other peoples, is a climato-topographical manifestation, just as is the case with the Egyptians, but for the opposite reason: the Egyptians suffer extreme heat, the Scythians extreme cold. The so-called Scythian desert is actually a grassy plateau, treeless, and moderately watered, since the large rivers drain water from the plains. The Nomadic Scyths who live in this region have no houses but live like gypsies in wagons, the smallest of which have four wheels, the others having six. The wagons are covered with felt cloths and may be divided like houses into two or three rooms; the roofs keep out rain, snow, and wind. Ox teams in two or three pairs draw the wagons about; the oxen are hornless because of the cold climate. The women live in the wagons, the men riding horseback, while their herds of sheep, cattle, and horses follow. Their stay in a given place is determined by the availability of pasture for their animals.   Their own diet consists (primarily?) of boiled meat (*krea hephtha*) and mares' milk, which also supplies them with a kind of cheese (*tyros*) called *hippake*.

The peculiarities of the Scythians, reflecting their climate, set them thus apart from all other peoples, and render them also very much like one another among their own kind. They are the least prolific of peoples; even their country produces very few wild animals and these are quite small in size. The reasons for these facts are to be sought in the position of the land, its exposure to the north and to the north wind, the brevity of summer which is commonly cool rather than not, and the combination of rain and mountains which makes much of the land uninhabitable. The plains are wrapped in fog during the day, prolonging winter; in addition, they are high and bare, and although they slope from the north, they are not wreathed by mountains. The wild animals in this region take shelter underground, as they are better enabled to do by their size which the climate has stunted. What contributes to the close resemblance to each other of the natives is the uniformity of the seasons in which the changes are few and not violent. Year in, year out their clothing and diet do not change, so slight is the variation in the seasons. The natives melt ice and snow for water and avoid physical exertion. As a result they are thick-skinned, fleshy, their joints do not show, and they are moist and unmuscular with extremely moist lower bowels. Since the seasons are so similar, the compaction of their seed (*he tou gonou sympexis*) takes place without corruption or deterioration, unless there is trauma or disease (chapter 19). Much of the description seems to fit the Tatars.

The odd statement is made that most Scyths, including all the Nomads, are *cauterized* (*kekaumenous,* if the manuscript tradition is correct) not only in the shoulders but also in the arms, wrists, chest, hips, and loins, "for no other reason than the moisture and softness of their nature." This moisture and lack of muscularity are the reason why they are unable to use the bow or throw the javelin, which is offset in part by the cauterization to which they subject themselves (cautery reduces the excess of moisture!). Because they do not have the custom of swaddling infants, and because of their sedentary way of life, their bodies are slack (*rhoika*) and squat (*platea*). Boys rarely walk as they usually ride in the wagons, and the girls are remarkably slack and flabby (*bladea*), or slow-moving (if the correct reading is *bradea*). The Scyths have a reddish complexion, as a result of the cold climate they live in (chapter 20).

A physical character of this sort makes high fertility impossible. The males have little sexual desire because of their moisture and because their bellies are soft and cold; these are the factors which militate most against sexual activity. Besides, their habit of riding horseback, with its constant jolting, is sexually weakening. Similarly, the women are too moist and fat to be fertile, since these qualities prevent the uterus from seizing and retaining the sperm. The same syndrome affects their menstruation. They are disincluned to exertion and fat, with bellies that are soft and cold. They are contrasted with their slave-girls, who are active and lean, and conceive very readily.

Most Scyths become eventually like eunuchs, perform the work of women, and work and talk like women. They are called *Anarieis*. The natives ascribe the cause of their impotence to a god and both revere and worship such men, out of fear for themselves. The writer agrees with the "divine origin" of these afflictions, but asserts that all afflictions are "divine" in origin, and none is more so than any other, nor more human either: *emoi de kai auto dokei tauta ta pathea theia einai kai talla panta kai ouden heteron heterou theioteron oude anthropinoteron, alla panta homoia kai panta theia.* The language of this passage has often recieved attention because in thought and to some extent in wording it duplicates that of chapters 1 and 21 of *Epilepsy: The Sacred Disease.* It is also of some anthropological interest that the Hippocratic writer's description of the *Anarieis* should resemble in so many ways the classic descriptions of the shaman, even though the phrase "most Scyths" (*hoi pleistoi en Skythesi*) seems on the face of it questionable.

Scythian eunuchism or impotence is further explained by the author of *AWP* as the consequence of genital swellings (*kedmata,* as interpreted by Littré, vol. 5, p. 320) caused by the Scythian habit of riding horseback constantly; severe cases were also marked by crippling lameness and hip sores. The cure which they adopted for this affliction was unfortunately worse than the disease which must have been, to be sure, quite painful. In my judgment, the passage has consistently been mistranslated by those who render the Greek word *ous* by the literal sense "ear." The passage, however, makes it quite certain that the reference intended by the author is to the *testis* or testicle, and this meaning should be added to the extended senses in which *ous* was used by the ancients.[6]

That the passage in question makes excellent sense rather than nonsense, if the proper meaning is given to the word *ous,* may be seen from the translation (see footnote).[7] Apparently, the duct referred to in the passage was the *ductus epididymidis,* though severing the *ductus* or *vas deferens* would lead to the same result: infertility. In any case, it is incredible that the Scythians or anyone else would cut "veins behind the ears" to relieve swelling in the genitals. The rendition in Jones's edition is thoroughly confused.

The chief significance of the passage, if this interpretation is correct, is the evidence which it adds to our understanding of the anatomical knowledge of the period in question (fifth and fourth centuries B.C.) and specifically to the fact that this knowledge was obtained by surgical procedures, as it could be based on no other means.

Modern statements about the practice of surgery in ancient times among the Greeks of the classical period are highly conflicting. Some of the most well-informed students of the subject have expressed great doubt that the Greeks had any subsurface knowledge of the human body, and that they pursued the twin discipline of anatomy and surgery in pre-Alexandrian times. This was, for example, the view of Charles Singer: "Anatomy and physiology, the basis of our modern system, was still a very weak point in the knowledge of the pre-Alexandrians. The surface form of the body was intimately studied in connexion expecially with fractures, but there is no evidence in the literature of the period of any closer acquaintance with human anatomical structure."[8]

A similar statement was made by Ludwig Edelstein: "The Hippocratics themselves never mention dissection of human cadavers. In their attempts to define the body, they make use only of external observation and of conclusions by analogy between human and animal organs. In the writing, *On ancient medicine,* the internal organs are described as they can be seen or palpated externally. The function of the internal organs is then determined by analogy to visible things: 'But one must become acquainted with it from outside by way of what can be seen.' . . ."[9]

The source of the argument over dissection, anatomy, and surgery by the Hippocratics is the second century (A.D.) writer, Galen: "One must conclude that Galen at any rate was of the opinion that the Hippocratics had already dissected humans" (Edelstein).[10] Edelstein was convinced that Galen's opinion was merely an attempt to explain the facts that he found incomprehensible, namely, the absence of anatomical textbooks in the writings of the Hippocratics. The arguments for and against the practice of surgery by the Hippocratics are reviewed at length by Edelstein in the work referred to. Edelstein's essential argument was that the dissection of human bodies could not take place until philosophy had disentangled itself from religious and popular feeling; this was a product of the fourth and third centuries B.C., which led to dissection in Alexandria in the third century, and its spread elsewhere; and it would also account for its dying out even there where it had begun, in the second century A.D.[11]

There is great additional interest in Edelstein's discussion nowadays for two reasons. The barbaric and inhumane practice of vivisection was prophetically yet unconsciously described by him in words which exactly fit the country he was to leave one year later: "(*Vivisections*) *could only be performed where an authoritarian state interested in science provided the means for them,* and for this reason they were performed only in Alexandria and at the beginning of the Hellenistic period, as Celsus says."[12] The second reason is the recurrent question of euthanasia and the new problem of organ transplants, particularly that of the heart—questions of life and death that go directly to our feelings about the body and its treatment (suggestive too of the concern of an earlier generation about inhumation and cremation). There seem to be, theoretically, *no* limits other than those which might be self-generating on the varieties of medical death and the disposition of bodies. Autopsy led very slowly to the willing of bodies for medical research; now "banks" exist for certain organs like the eye, and most recently proposals have been announced for multiorgan depositories.

I have digressed enough to show that the surgical question insofar as it relates to the Hippocratics is yet unresolved, despite the conviction or confidence on either side. However, the same passage in *AWP* (chapter 22), with which this discussion began, reveals a further confusion. Immediately after stating that the cutting of the testicular ducts (spermatic ducts) causes sterility, the writer says that the treatment results in *impotence:* "Following this treatment, when they resort to women and cannot have intercourse with them, at first they do not pay much attention and say nothing about it. However, after two, three, or more attempts lead to the same result, they conclude that they have offended the god, whom they consider responsible, and they put on female dress, in recognition of their loss of virility. They behave like women and perform the same work that women do."[13]

That the writer has confused sterility with impotence is easy enough to see but difficult to explain, unless we assume psychogenic impotence following the trauma of surgery; even so, this would leave more than one question unanswered, which the paucity of information given by the writer of *AWP* only underscores.

The double affliction of sterility and impotence is related by the writer to the caste system prevalent among the Scyths: the upper classes (*hoi eugenestatoi*) ride horseback, they are in fact the rich (*hoi plousioi*); the poor (*hoi penetes*), who form the lowest class (*hoi kakistoi*) do not ride horseback and so are less affected. The writer uses this fact to strike down the notion that the disease is more divine than any other: their wealth and their offerings to the gods would in that case make them immune to the affliction. The truth is that the disease is natural (*kata physin*) and no more divine or less divine than any other. In fact, wherever the same complex situation occurs, the result is the same, not only among Scyths: prolonged riding at frequent intervals is the initiating factor which leads to genital swellings, sciatica, gout, and sexual incapacity. Contributing factors are the wearing of britches or trousers together with the constant horseback riding and the resultant lack of handling the genitals, plus subjection to cold and fatigue; all these make men forgetful of sexual activity and even lose interest or desire for it (perhaps the same description could be applied to the western cowboys of modern times).

That the Scyths were caste-ridden in some remarkable degree appears to be borne out by both ancient and modern commentators. Among the latter, the Scyths are associated with the Hindus, whose caste system is both ancient and notorious.[14]

The fluctuation in attribution of causes noticeable in *AWP,* as in other parts of the Hippocratic Collection, is not merely a stylistic feature, but also reflects the thought processes of the individual contributors to the Collection. Perhaps it is only a recognition of the many factors which cooperate to produce a given condition, disease, or entity whatever. So in chapter 23, where the author resumes the central theory of discussion in the latter half of *AWP,* the general statement is repeated, that the differences from one another among the peoples of Europe are to be explained by the violence and frequency of the seasonal changes to which they are exposed. Then there is added to this a correlated cause: "A natural consequence of these changes is the variable development in the composition (*sympexis*) of seed, which is affected differently in summer from the way in which it is affected in winter, differently in times of heavy rains from times of drought" (see chapter 19, discussed above). Hence the greater physical variation among Europeans than that found among Asians: the former differ from each other from one city to the next, even in size.

The same explanation applies to character (*ethe,* plural of *ethos*). The climate of Europe accounts for the wild, unsociable, and passionate temper of those subject to it, since constant shocks to the mind implant savagery, whereas they extirpate tameness and gentleness. It also accounts for the writer's belief that the inhabitants of Europe are more courageous than those of Asia (Minor). Idleness and easygoing mode of existence inhere in a state of relative equilibrium, whereas change is productive of exertion and endurance for both body and soul. Thus, to sum up the author's arguments without repeating them all in detail as he does, climate produces a certain physique and a certain character or termperament; but it also encourages the establishment of certain customs and these in turn reinforce character (again using the instance of rule by kings among the Asians to account for their cowardice which is stigmatized as extreme: *hokou gar basileuontai, ekei ananke deilotatous einai*). These ideas have become the common staple of discussion with regard to the distinctions among peoples in different climates.

The writer has given us a conspectus of the differences among Europeans in correlation with those that obtain among them in climate. The European tribes differ in size, shape, and manliness, or courage. If the region is mountainous, rugged, lofty, and well watered, with sharp variations in the seasonal changes, the natives will tend to be tall, hardy, virile or courageous, with no small degree of wildness and ferocity.

In contrast, the natives of regions which are in valleys or lowlands (literally, "hollows": *koila choria*), filled with meadows, and stifling, with more hot winds than cool, and using hot waters, tend to broadness, they are fleshy and dark-haired, with dark complexions, more bilious than phlegmatic. They naturally lack courage and hardihood, but these may be imposed by their customs (*nomos*:

Jones translates as "law"). If the region lacks rivers and the drinking water is stagnant, the people are bound to display swollen bellies and enlarged spleens.

If they live on a high plateau which is open to the winds and well watered, they will be tall and resemble one another, but they will also be rather lacking in courage and rather tame in spirit.

Where the land is thin, dry, and bare, with sharp contrasts in the changes of the seasons, the natives are apt to be tough, sinewy, fair-complexioned, and stubborn and independent in their character and temper.

In sum, the chief cause of variation in the physical makeup of populations is the seasonal changes; second, the land in which one grows up; and third, the waters. The final chapter (24) of *AWP* ends with these remarks: "For you will find on the whole that both the physical characteristics of men and their ways are intimately dependent on the nature of the land. In fact, where the land is fertile, free of stones, and well-watered, and the water table close to the surface so that it is warmed in summer and cooled in winter, and the land is well situated with regard to the seasons, the natives are fleshy, with their joints deep in fat, and they are moist, ill suited for exertion, and in general cowardly in disposition. They display laziness and sleepiness to the observer, and they are thick-witted rather than subtle or quick in the arts.

"But where the land is bare, unwatered, rugged, and buffeted by wintry weather or baked by the heat of the sun, there you will see men who are tough, spare, limber, muscular, and hairy. Such men exhibit industriousness, and alertness. In character and temper they are wilful and hold their own opinions. They are savage rather than tame, and you will find them to be quicker in the arts, more intelligent, and braver in warfare than others.

Indeed, everything else that is produced on earth is adapted to it. The most opposite natures and forms are as we have described them. If you base your considerations of the rest upon judgments derived from these observations, you will not go wrong."[15]

Notes and References

Chapter One

1. Ludwig Edelstein, "Nachträge (Hippokrates)," *Paulys Real-Encyclopädie der classischen Altertumswissenschaft*, Neue Bearbeitung, Supplementband VI (1935), column 1293.

2. Giovanni Becatti, "Il ritratto di Ippocrate," Pontificia Accademia Romana di Archeologia, *Rendiconti* 21, Ser. 3 (1945/6), pp. 123–41.

3. Louis Bourgey, *Observation et expérience chez les médecins de la Collection Hippocratique* (Paris, 1953), Librairie J. Vrin, pp. 86–96.

4. Edelstein, *op. cit.*, column 1332; W. H. S. Jones, translator, *Hippocrates*, Vol. I (Loeb Classical Library; Cambridge, Mass., 1923), "General Introduction," pp. xxviii ff.

5. *Ibid.*, p. xxviii.

6. See Emile Littré, editor and translator, *Oeuvres complètes d'Hippocrate*, Vol. I (Paris, 1839), "Introduction," p. 293, and the discussion which follows.

7. Edelstein, *op. cit.*, column 1331.

Chapter Two

1. The importance of this statement is indicated by its reiteration in several chapters of the essay; see also chapters 2, 8, 12 (in which the basis of medical achievement is called *logismos*, i.e., "reasoning"), 13, and 15.

2. *Ancient Medicine*, chapter 24: *beltiston de esti aiei to prosotate tou anepitedeiou apechon.*

3. W. H. S. Jones, *Hippocrates*, II, 195 (footnote).

4. Littré wrongly summarized this definition by saying "its object is to cure illness (*Oeuvres complètes d'Hippocrate*, VI, p. 5)!

5. Walter Modell, *Relief of Symptoms*, 2nd ed. (C. V. Mosby, 1961), p. 13.

6. *The Art of Medicine*, chapter 7: *thelontes ta pros ten nouson ede mallon e pros ten hygieinen prosdechesthai* (translated by Jones as "wishful of treatment rather to enjoy immediate alleviation of his sickness than to recover his health").

7. See Edwin B. Levine and Myra E. Levine, "Hippocrates, Father of

Nursing, Too?" *American Journal of Nursing,* LXV (December, 1965), 86–88.

8. Jones, *op. cit.,* Vol. II, p. 187.

9. *Regimen, I,* chapter 12: *Ego de deloso technas phaneras anthropou pathemasin homoias eousas kai phaneroisi kai aphanesi.* Elsewhere I have used "experience" to translate the term *pathemasin.* Jones's rendition is recurrently opaque.

10. The title is discussed by W. H. S. Jones in the fourth volume of his edition of selections from the Hippocratic Collection, pp. xxx–xxxii.

11. See Littré, *op. cit.,* Vol. I, p. 88.

12. Jones, *op. cit.,* Vol I, "General Introduction," p. liii.

13. On this chapter in general, cf. Littré, *op. cit.,* Vol. I, pp. 440–64. Ideas survive like genes in the population: see William Madsen, *Mexican-Americans of South Texas,* "Case Studies in Cultural Anthropology" (New York, 1964), pp. 70–71, where the humoral theory is called a "legacy from colonial Mexico where the Spaniards introduced the system of Hippocratic medicine in the sixteenth century." Also, Madsen's statement that "Hippocratic medicine still flourishes in rural Mexico but is dying out among the Latins in south Texas" (*ibid.*).

Chapter Three

1. The phrase was borrowed from Cato the Elder: see Pliny the Younger, *Epistulae,* 4.7.5 and Quintilian, *Inst. Or.,* 12.1.1.

2. *Professional Conduct (Peri euschemosynes),* chapter 1.

3. Allegedly, the hero Asklepios was apothesized late in the fifth century B.C. Perhaps this culmination influenced the physician who wrote *Professional Conduct.* It is even conceivable that his writing in some way aided that apotheosis. The reader is referred to two modern assessments of Asklepios: (1) *Asclepius: A Collection and Interpretation of the Testimonies,* by Emma J. Edelstein and Ludwig Edelstein, especially Vol. II (1945), p. 66; and (2) Karl Karenyi's *Der göttliche Arzt* (1956), pp. 67–69.

4. *Professional Conduct (Peri euschemosynes),* chapter 5.

Chapter Four

1. I have discussed the twin aspects of professionalism and practice surveyed in chapters 3 and 4 of this book, in a paper delivered November 7, 1969, at a meeting of the Illinois Classical Conference. Space does not permit me to incorporate my remarks here.

Chapter Five

1. In *Forschungen zur antiken Sklaverei,* Band II, Franz Steiner Verlag Gmbh., Wiesbaden (1968), p. 44 and *passim.*

2. Cf. Jones, *op. cit.*, Vol. IV, "Introduction," pp. lii–liii.

3. *Dreams* (same as *Regimen,* Book IV), chapter 86. Cf. Sigmund Freud's remarks: "And what of the value of dreams in regard to our knowledge of the future? That, of course, is quite out of the question. One would like to substitute the words: 'in regard to our knowledge of the past.' For in every sense a dream has its origin in the past. The ancient belief that dreams reveal the future is not indeed entirely devoid of truth. By representing a wish as fulfilled the dream certainly leads us into the future; but this future, which the dreamer accepts as his present, has been shaped in the likeness of the past by the indestructible wish" (from the conclusion to "The Interpretation of Dreams," in *The Basic Writings of Sigmund Freud,* translated and edited with an introduction by Dr. A. A. Brill, New York: The Modern Library, c. 1938, p. 549). The last two sentences of this quotation are used by Leslie Fiedler in an article on dreamers and the literary life, entitled "Master of Dreams" (*Partisan Review,* XXXIV, no. 3, 1967 (Summer), p. 356.

4. See Littré, *op. cit.*, Vol. VII, pp. 304–9. Fuller inquiry cannot be pursued here, but the question is one of interest and importance.

5. Ludwig Edelstein, *Ancient Medicine: Selected Papers of Ludwig Edelstein* (1967), p. 370; a posthumous collection of essays by the outstanding investigator in this century of the Hippocratic Collection.

6. Littré, *op. cit.*, Vol. VII, p. 164 and p. 309.

7. *Ibid.,* p. 309.

8 For the observational powers of the Hippocratics, as exemplified by not only the case histories but most other writings discussed in this chapter, see Walther Riese's introductory remarks in *Galen: On the Passions and Errors of the Soul,* translated by Paul W. Harkins, with an introduction and interpretation by Walther Riese (Ohio State University Press, 1963), pp. 10–12.

Chapter Six

1. See also René Dubos, *So Human an Animal* (1968), esp. p. 47 and p. 95, for comments laudatory of the essay *Airs, Waters, Places.*

2. Cf. the phrase of the poet Horace: *dominus terrae fastidiosus* ("the owner contemptuous of the land"), which appears in the first Roman Ode, *Carmina,* 3.1.36–37.

3. As cited in Robert Joly, *Le niveau de la science hippocratique: Contribution à la psychologie de l'histoire des sciences* (1966), p. 180. Joly characterizes even the best parts of the Hippocratic Collection as "pre-scientific."

4. *Ibid.,* p. 183 and p. 187. See also in particular Ludwig Edelstein, "*Peri aeron* und die Sammlung der Hippokratischen Schriften," *Problemata: Forschungen zur klassischen Philologie,* Heft 4 (1931), p. 60.

Edelstein concluded that *AWP* is composed of two essays, one medical, the other geographical, the union of which is accidental.

5. Cf. the article "Scythia" in the *Encyclopaedia Britannica* (c.1960), vol. 20, p. 235.

6. These extended meanings are given in Liddell-Scott, *Greek-English Lexicon,* p. 1274; see also the reference given there under II.2 to *parotis* (p. 1345).

7. "At the onset of this ailment, they sever the duct behind each testicle. When the flow of blood stops, drowziness overcomes them from their weakness and they fall asleep. On awakening, some may be cured, some may not. To me it seems that the sperm is destroyed by this treatment, for alongside the testicles are ducts, and if anyone cut them, those operated on will not produce sperm. So I believe it is these ducts which they cut" (translation mine).

8. From Singer's essay on "Medicine," in *The Legacy of Greece,* edited by R. W. Livingstone (Oxford, 1922), p. 216.

9. *Ancient Medicine: Selected Papers of Ludwig Edelstein,* edited by Owsei Temkin and C. Lilian Temkin, Baltimore (1967), p. 253; also the statements made on pp. 255, 256, 257. (This essay by Edelstein was originally published in German under the title, "Die Geschichte der Sektion in der Antike," in Quellen *und Studien zur Geschichte der Naturwissenschaft und der Medizin,* Band 3, Heft 2, Berlin (1932), pp. 100–156). These statements in particular deserve consideration: "the Hippocratic physicians themselves did not dissect humans. They gained their knowledge from chance observation and from animal dissection" (p. 255); and, "the assertion that the Hippocratic physicians practiced anatomy is merely an unprovable contention" (p. 256).

10. *Op. cit.,* p. 257.

11. *Ibid.,* pp. 273–85.

12. *Ibid.,* p. 297; italics mine.

13. *AWP,* chapter 22 (lines 27–36 of the Loeb edition; the translation is mine).

14. Cf. the conclusions attributed to Thomas W. Clark, by Carleton S. Coon, author, with Edward E. Hunt, Jr., of *The Living Races of Man* (1965), pp. 204-5. See also Theodosius Dobzhansky, *Mankind Evolving; The Evolution of the Human Species* (New Haven and London, 1962), pp. 234–38. The genetic view of the latter reinforces the conclusions of ethnography and anthropology, as well as the historical record, fragmentary though it is.

15. *AWP,* chapter 24 (lines 43–67 of the Loeb edition; the translation is mine).

Selected Bibliography

PRIMARY SOURCES

GALEN. *Galeni in Hippocratis De officina medici commentariorum versionem arabican, quoad exstat, ex codice scorialensi et excerpta, quae 'Ali Ibn Ridwan ex eis sumpsit, ex codice cantabrigensi edidit et in linguam anglicam vertit Malcolm Lyons.* Berolini in aedibus Academiae Scientiarum MCMLXIII (*Corpus medicorum Graecorum Supplementum orientale ediderunt Academiae Berolinensis Haviensis Lipsiensis,* I . . .).

―――. *Galeni in Hippocratis Epidemiarum libros commentaria. Indices nominum et verborum Graecorum composuerunt Ernst Wenkebach, Konrad Schubring. Corpus medicorum Graecorum ediderunt Academiae Berolinensis Havniensis Lipsiensis,* V 10, 2, 3. Berolini in aedibus Academiae Litterarum, MCMLV, Lipsiae: Typis B. G. Teubneri, Akademie-Verlag GMBH Berlin.

―――. *On the passions and errors of the soul. Translated by Paul W. Harkins with an Introduction and Interpretation by Walther Riese.* (place not given): Ohio State University Press, 1963 ("fully authorized translation of the original edition which was published by the B. G. Teubner Publishing Company").

HIPPOCRATES. *Ancient Medicine and Other Treatises.* Chicago, Illinois: Henry Regnery Company, for The Great Books Foundation, 1949 ("translation used in this edition, except for some slight revisions, is that of Francis Adams").

―――. *The Genuine Works of Hippocrates translated from the Greek with a Preliminary Discourse and Annotations by Francis Adams, LL.D., Surgeon.* New York: William Wood & Company, 1886. Two vols. in one.

―――. *Medical Works. A new translation by John Chadwick and W. N. Mann.* Oxford: Blackwell, 1950.

―――. *Hippocrates with an English translation by W. H. S. Jones.* Cambridge, Mass.: Harvard University Press, 1962. (*Loeb Classical Library;* 4 vols., originally published 1923–31; vol. III [1928] is the work of Dr. E. T. Withington).

―――. HIPPOCRATIS COI APHORISMI *Cum Concordantia eorum-*

dem ac indice locupletissimo. Accedunt iidem APHORISMI Versu heroico explicati à JOANN. BAPT. CONDÉ Medico Bruxellensi. Lovanii: Apud J. P. G. Michel, Bibliopolam, M. DCC. LXXXI.

―――――. MAGNI HIPPOCRATIS MEDICORUM OMNIUM FACILE PRINCIPIS, OPERA OMNIA quae extant In VIII SECTIONES ex Erotiani mente distributa. *NUNC RECENS LATIna interpretatione donata, ac denuò separatim in lucem edita.* ANUTIO FOESIO Mediomatrico Medico Authore: *Adiecta sunt ad* VI *Sectionem Palladii Scholia in lib. de Fracturis, nondum antea excussa, & 'nunc primùm è Graeco in Latinum conversa.* Cum INDICE amplissimo & vtilissimo. Francofurti: Apud her. And. Wechli, Claud, Marni & Io. Aubr., M. D. XCVI. *Cum priuilegio S. Caesareae Maiestatis.*

―――――. *OEuvres complètes d'Hippocrate, Traduction nouvelle avec le texte grec en regard, collationné sur les manuscrits et toutes les éditions; accompagnée d'une introduction, de commentaires médicaux, de variantes et de notes philologiques;* Suivie d'une table générale des matières. Par É. Littré. Amsterdam: Adolf M. Hakkert, Éditeur, 1961–62 ("Réimpression anastatique de l'Edition, Paris 1839" – 61).

―――――. (*Peri hieres nousou*). *Die hippokratische Schrift* "Über die heilige Krankheit." Herausgegeben, übersetzt und erläutert von Hermann Grensemann. Berlin: Walter de Gruyter & Co., 1968, c1967. (*Ars Medica, Texte und Untersuchungen zur Quellenkunde der Alten Medizin, Schriftenreihe des Instituts für Geschichte der Medizin der Freien Universität Berlin,* II. *Abteilung, Griechischlateinische Medizin,* herausgeben von Karl Deichgräber, Hans Diller, Heinz Goreke, Band I. First volume in the latest attempt in the last century and a half of Hippocratic research to launch a comprehensive investigation encompassing the most recent research as well as the research of preceding generations in hopes of producing a viable text of major Greek medical writings; this vol. is by the editor of the (Pseudo-) Hippocratic *De septimestri partu* and the Hippocratic *De octimestri partu* for the *Corpus Medicorum Graecorum* (I 2, 1), 1968, based on his 1960 dissertation, and is a text edition with translation and notes; also includes an essay (pp. 5–30) on the position of *De morbo sacro* (*The Sacred Disease,* or *Epilepsy*) in ancient medicine and another on the Sources of the Text and the Text or MS. Tradition (pp. 31–55).

SECONDARY SOURCES

BECATTI, GIOVANNI. "Il ritratto di Ippocrate," *Pontificia Accademia Romana di Archeologia, Rendiconti* 21, *Ser.* 3, 1945/6, pp. 123–41.

Report of the discovery of a bust of Ostia during World War II believed by its discoverer to be that of Hippocrates with the arguments for its genuineness. Portrait reproduced in Scarborough (see entry, below).

BIER, AUGUST. "Hippokratische Studien," *Quellen und Studien zur Geschichte der Naturwissenschaften und der Medizin*, Bd. 3 (1933), zweites Heft, pp. 1–28 (51–78). Bier was a physician who contributed several papers to Greek medical origins.

BIÖRCK, GUNNAR. "Thoughts on Life and Death," *Perspectives in Biology and Medicine*, Summer, 1968, Vol. II, No. 4, pp. 527–43. Revision of a paper presented at the First World Meeting on Medical Law in Ghent, Belgium, August, 1967. "The Swedish physician is not officially requested to take the Hippocratic oath or any of its modern equivalents" (p. 527). A topical commentary from the Swedish physician's point of view of euthanasia, and a topic on which the literature continues to grow at an increasing rate.

BORDONOVE, GEORGES. *Molière génial et familier.* Paris; Ottowa: Robert Laffont; Le Cercle du livre de France, 1967, 1968. See especially Ch. xxii, "Molière et les médecins," pp. 304–14, and references, *passim,* to Molière's medical plays and views.

BOURGEY, LOUIS. *Observation et expérience chez les médecins de la Collection Hippocratique.* Paris: Librairie Philosophique J. Vrin, 1953. A useful inquiry into two related aspects of Hippocratic medicine.

COON, CARLETON S., with HUNT, EDWARD E., JR. *The Living Races of Man.* New York: Alfred A. Knopf, 1965. Contains a brief but interesting passage on the Sanskritic relatives of the Scyths and Sarmatians.

DEICHGRÄBER, KARL. "Die Epidemien und das Corpus Hippocraticum. Voruntersuchungen zu einer Geschichte der koischen Ärzteschule." Berlin: Verlag der Akademie der Wissenschaften in Kommission bei Walter de Gruyter und Co., 1933. (*Abhandlungen der preussischen Akademie der Wissenschaften,* Jahrgang 1933, philosophisch-historische Klasse, Nr. 3, pp. 1–172.) Discusses the *Epidemics* in relation to the received notions about Coan medicine.

DER KLEINE PAULY. *Lexikon der Antike auf der Grundlage von Pauly's Realencyclopädie der classischen Altertumswissenschaft unter Mitwirkung zahlreicher Fachgelehrter bearbeitet und herausgegeben von Konrat Ziegler und Walther Sontheimer.* Stuttgart: Alfred Druckenmüller Verlag. (Bd. I published 1964: "Aachen bis Dichalkon;" Bd. II published 1967: "Dicta Catonis bis Iuno;" Bd. III published 1969: "Iuppiter bis Nasidienus;" the entire work to be complete in five vols.) Summary up-to-date articles on classical antiquity with select major bibliography of important research contributions from the scholarly literature.

DILLER, HANS. "Stand und Aufgaben der Hippokratesforschung." *Akademie der Wissenschaften und Literatur, Mainz, Jahrbuch. NST* 1950–60, pp. 271–87. Wiesbaden: 1959. Present status and future requirements of research on the Hippocratic Collection are briefly reviewed.

DOBZHANSKY, THEODOSIUS. *Mankind Evolving. The Evolution of the Human Species.* New Haven and London: Yale University Press, c1962. (Originally published as a Silliman Foundation Lecture.) A discussion of human genetics: of relevance for the understanding of the Hippocratic *Airs, Waters, Places.*

DRABKIN, MIRIAM. "A Select Bibliography of Greek and Roman Medicine," *Bulletin of the History of Medicine,* XI (1942), pp. 399–408.

DUBOS, RENÉ. *Man Adapting.* New Haven and London: Yale University Press, 1965. (*Yale University, Mrs. Hepsa Ely Silliman Memorial Lectures,* vol. 39.) A discussion of man and environment by the Rockefeller University microbiologist from the adaptive point of view.

————. "Man and His Environment—Biomedical Knowledge and Social Action," *Perspectives in Biology and Medicine,* IX (Summer, 1966), pp. 523–36. Dubos is a major spokesman of a rationalist ecology.

————. "Hippocrates in Modern Dress," *Perspectives in Biology and Medicine,* IX (Winter, 1966), pp. 275–88. The Hippocratic contribution evaluated by a distinguished researcher.

————. *So Human an Animal.* New York: Charles Scribner's Sons, 1968. Observations on man the product of his environment, by the most preëminent of modern Hippocratists.

EDELSTEIN, E. J. and EDELSTEIN, L. *Asclepios. A Collection and Interpretation of the Testimonies.* 2 vols. Baltimore: The Johns Hopkins University Press, 1945. An important basic collection of source materials on Asklepios (Aesculapius).

EDELSTEIN, LUDWIG. *Ancient Medicine. Selected Papers of Ludwig Edelstein,* edited by Owsei Temkin and C. Lilian Temkin. Translations from the German by C. Lilian Temkin. Baltimore: The Johns Hopkins Press, 1967. A commemorative volume of original papers by the best and most influential skeptic expositor of Hippocratic doctrine.

————. "Die Geschichte der Sektion in der Antike," *Quellen und Studien zur Geschichte der Naturwissenschaften und der Medizin,* Bd. 3, Heft 2, pp. 50–106. Berlin: Julius Springer, 1932 (pp. 100–156 of the vol.). An interpretation of the evidence for both dissection and vivisection of animals and humans based on E.'s conviction that vivisections "could only be performed where an authoritarian state interested in science provided the means for them" (v. his *Ancient Medicine, supra*, p. 297).

————. *The Hippocratic Oath. Text, translation, and interpretation.* Baltimore: The Johns Hopkins Press, 1943. (*Supplements to the Bulletin of the History of Medicine*, No. 1.) Discussion and conclusions on the basis of the text and related evidence.

————. *The Idea of Progress in Classical Antiquity.* Baltimore: The Johns Hopkins Press, 1967. Posthumous work showing the extension of E.'s lifework in Greek medicine to research in the complex roots of progressivism.

————. "Nachträge (Hippokrates)," *Pauly-Wissowa Realencyclopädie, Supplementband* VI, cols. 1290–1345. Stuttgart: J. B. Metzler, 1935. A fifty-six column supplement updating H. Gossen's fifty-two column article in review of the evidence and research published 24 years previous in the main vol.

————. *PERI 'AERON und die Sammlung der Hippokratischen Schriften.* Berlin: 1931. (*Problemata: Forschungen zur klassischen Philologie, Heft 4.*) The relationship of *Airs, Waters, Places* to the Hippocratic Corpus.

FARRINGTON, BENJAMIN. *Greek Science: Its Meaning for Us. Vol. One: Thales to Aristotle; Vol. Two: Theophrastus to Galen.* Harmondsworth, Middlesex: Penguin Books, 1944, 1949. An introductory survey of Greek science including medicine.

FLASHAR, HELLMUT. *Melancholie und Melancholiker in den medizinischen Theorien der Antike.* Berlin: Walter de Gruyter & Co., 1966. A greatly expanded treatment of the subject of F.'s *Habilitationsvortrag* (1961) exploring the doctrine of humors including melancholia and its evolvement into modern therapy.

GARRISON, FIELDING H. *An Introduction to the History of Medicine with Medical Chronology, Suggestions for Study and Bibliographic Data.* Fourth edition, reprinted. Philadelphia and London: W. B. Saunders Company, 1929 (reprinted 1966). Standard reference work in medical history.

GOMPERZ, THEODOR. *Die Apologie der Heilkunst, eine griechische Sophistenrede des fünften vorchristlichen Jahrhunderts, bearbeitet übersetzt, erläutert und eingeleitet von Theodor Gomperz.* Zweite durchgesehene Auflage. Leipzig: Verlag von Veit & Company, 1910. (The first printing of this important discussion of *The Art of Medicine*, in Greek *Peri Technes*, appeared in the *Sitzungsberichte der Kais. Akademie der Wissenschaften in Wien, philosophisch-historische Classe*, Band CXX, IX, Wien: In Commission bei F. Tempsky, Buchändler der. Kais. Akademie der Wissenschaften,

1890, pp. 1–196.) Gomperz, born March 29, 1832 in Brünn (now Brno, Czechoslovakia), then part of the Austrian Empire, remains one of the great students of the Hippocratic Collection.

————. "Die Hippokratische Frage und der Ausgangspunkt ihrer Lösung," *Philologus*, LXX (1911), Leipzig. Discussion of a possible basis for resolution of the Hippocratic enigma.

GOSSEN, H. "Hippokrates," *Pauly-Wissowa Realencyclopädie der classischen Altertumswissenschaft*, Band VIII, cols. 1801–1852. Stuttgart: J. B. Metzler, 1911. The basic statement of all that was known or conjectured about the Hippocratic Collection up to its time of publication, presented in typical highly condensed but meaty form.

GUTHRIE, W. K. C. *A History of Greek Philosophy*. Vol. I: *The Earlier Presocratics and the Pythagoreans;* Vol. II: *The Presocratic Tradition from Parmenides to Democritus;* Vol. III: *The Fifth-Century Enlightenment* (all published to date; to be complete in six volumes). Cambridge: At the University Press; Vol. I, 1962, reprinted 1967; Vol. II, 1965; Vol. III, 1969. The most recent standard work on the subject and period in English.

HEIDEL, W. A. *Hippocratic Medicine: Its Spirit and Method*. New York: 1941. For discussion of psychic factors see pp. 129f. ftn. 34 and p. 130 ftn. 35.

JOLY, ROBERT. *Hippocrate. Médecine grecque.* (place not given): Gallimard, c1964. ("Collection Idées.") An anthology of selections from the Hippocratic Corpus with brief interconnecting commentary by J.

————. *Le niveau de la science hippocratique. Contribution à la psychologie de l'histoire des sciences.* Paris: Société d'Édition *"LES BELLES LETTRES,"* 1966. A discussion in eight chapters of the scientific value of several Hippocratic essays. The author is Chargé de cours au Centre Universitaire de Mons and at the Université Libre de Bruxelles.

————. *Recherches sur le traité pseudo-hippocratique Du Régime.* Paris: Société d'Édition "Les Belles Lettres," 1960. (Bibliothèque de la Faculté de Philosophie et Lettres de l'Université de Liège, Fascicule CLVI.) A *thèse d'agrégation de l'Enseignement Supérieur* devoted to a philological examination of *Peri diaites*.

KATZ, ARNOLD M. and KATZ, PHYLLIS B. "Diseases of the Heart in the Works of Hippocrates," *British Heart Journal,* 24:3 (1962), pp. 257–64. Discussion by a cardiologist and a classicist: they elicit from the Corpus "clinical descriptions recognizable as heart failure, Adams-Stokes syndrome, Cheyne-Stokes respiration, rheumatic fever, and cardiac pain" (p. 264).

KERÉNYI, K. *Der göttliche Arzt.* Zweite Auflage. Darmstadt: Wissenschaftliche Buchgesellschaft, 1956. The deification of the doctor-hero. K. accepts as genuine the portrait bust of Hippocrates found by Becatti, p. 108 ftn. 99. See also p. 70 remarks on *Abb.* 45.

KIND, FRIEDRICH ERNST. "Bericht über die Literatur zur antiken Medizin 1911–1917," *Jahresbericht für Altertumswissenschaft,* Bd. 180 (1919. III), pp. 1–108. A meticulous review of the research on ancient medicine for the period is indicated.

KNUTZEN, GEORG. "Technologie in den hippokratischen Schriften *Peri diaites oxeon, Peri agmon, Peri arthron emboles.* Wiesbaden: Verlag der Akademie der Wissenschaften und der Literatur in Mainz in Kommission bei Franz Steiner Verlag GMBH. (*Abhandlungen der Geistes-und Sozialwissenschaftlichen Klasse,* Jahrgang 1963, Nr. 14.) An exploration of the concept *techne.*

KUDLIEN, FRIDOLF. *Der Beginn des medizinischen Denkens bei den Griechen von Homer bis Hippokrates.* Zürich und Stuttgart: Artemis Verlag, 1967. (*Die Bibliothek der alten Welt, Reihe Forschung und Deutung.*) Essay on pre-Hippocratic thought in Greece. Has appendix of Greek and Latin texts with translations in German (pp. 155–67).

————. "Die Sklaven in der griechischen Medizin der klassischen und hellenistischen Zeit," *Forschungen zur antiken Sklaverei,* im Auftrag der Kommission für Geschichte des Altertums der Akademie der Wissenschaften und der Literatur (Mainz), herausgegeben von Joseph Vogt und Hans Ulrich Instinsky, Band II. Wiesbaden: Franz Steiner Verlag GMBH, 1968. Discusses status of slaves and freeborn vis-à-vis medical practice, slaves as patients, and the problem of slaves as physicians in the classical period.

LAUER, HANS H., M.D. "Zahl und Medizin," *Janus, Revue internationale de l'histoire des sciences, de la médecine, de la pharmacie, et de la technique,* LIII, 3 (1966), pp. 161–93. The position of number in the medicine of antiquity, the Renaissance, and today by a staff member of the Institut für Geschichte der Medizin der Universität Heidelberg.

LEVINE, EDWIN B. and LEVINE, MYRA E. "Hippocrates, Father of Nursing, Too?" *American Journal of Nursing,* Vol. 65 (December, 1965), pp. 86–88. The evidence of the Hippocratic Collection supports the conclusion that the "Father of Medicine" may have fathered Nursing as well.

LIVINGSTONE, R. W. *The Legacy of Greece.* Oxford: The Clarendon Press, 1922. Important articles on the Greek contributions to Biology and Medicine by Charles Singer, Lecturer in the History of Medicine in University College, London. (See also entries below under Singer.)

LLOYD, G. E. R. *Polarity and Analogy: Two Types of Argumentation in Early Greek Thought.* New York: Cambridge University Press, 1966. Careful examination of thought processes in early Greek writers with much that is directly relevant to the understanding of the Hippocratics. Reviewed in *Classical Journal,* vol. 62, no. 7 (April, 1967), pp. 316–18.

LONIE, I. M. "Medical Theory in Heraclides of Pontus," *Mnemosyne, Bibliotheca Classica Batava,* Series IV, Volumen XVIII, Fasciculus 2 (1965), pp. 126–43. Lugduni Batavorum: E. J. Brill. Professor Lonie of The University of Otago (New Zealand) examines inter-relationships between the philosopher Heraclides (Herakleides) Ponticus, ca. 390–310 B.C. and, among others, the first-century B.C. practitioner (in Rome), Asclepiades of Prusa in Bithynia.

LOUIS, A. "Analyse des bibliothèques de deux médecins malinois du 15e Siècle," *Janus, Revue internationale de l'histoire des sciences, de la médecine, de la pharmacie et de la technique,* LIII, 4 (1966), pp. 241–305. Both doctors had the *Aphorismi* and the six books of *Epidemics;* Simon de Slusa's library also contained the *Prognostica secreta.* De Slusa, who in addition to being a doctor had also the degree *maître ès Arts,* had a medical collection of 133 different works; Van Malderen, the other doctor, lacking the second degree, had half as many medical titles in his possession. Attention is called to M. Louis to the striking fact that both collections attest the currency if not supremacy of Greek medical thought even after the Renaissance (pp. 302–3).

MADSEN, WILLIAM. "Mexican-Americans of South Texas," *Case Studies in Cultural Anthropology.* New York (etc.): Holt, Rinehart and Winston, c1964. Monograph reveals persistence of the Hippocratic humoral theory in the folk medicine of the Latins in North America in the twentieth century.

MARROU, HENRI-IRÉNÉE. *A History of Education in Antiquity. Translated by George Lamb.* New York: The New American Library, c1956 (translated from *Histoire de l'Education dans l'Antiquité,* 3rd ed., Editions du Seuil, Paris, and published by Sheed & Ward, Inc.; Mentor Book 1st printing January, 1964). Marrou, Professor of Early Christian History at the Sorbonne, says of the ancient physicians from Hippocrates to Galen that they appear to "have been continually dogged by an inferiority complex" vis-à-vis their philosopic confrères, p. 303.

MODELL, WALTER. *Relief of Symptoms.* Second edition. St. Louis: The C. V. Mosby Company, 1961. Dr. Modell, Director of Clinical Pharmacology and Associate Professor of Pharmacology at Cornell

University Medical College when this book was written, explores the "dichotomy of cure and relief" in modern medical practice.

OPPENHEIMER, A. LEO. *Ancient Mesopotamia. Portrait of a Dead Civilization.* Chicago & London: The University of Chicago Press, 1964. Interesting discussion by the Assyriologist of the medical practice of Mesopotamia and the roles of *asû* (physician), *asipu* (conjurer), and *asû agasgû* (apprentice physician), pp. 289–305.

OSLER, SIR WILLIAM. *Aequanimitas, with other Addresses to Medical Students, Nurses and Practitioners of Medicine.* Third edition. Philadelphia: The Blakiston Company, 1932 (reprinted 1943). Animadversions on the life devoted to medicine by one peculiarly inspired by the Greek ideal.

———. *A Way of Life, and Selected Writings of Sir William Osler,* July 12, 1849 to December 29, 1919. (Formerly entitled *Selected Writings of Sir William Osler.*) With an introduction by G. L. Keynes, M.D., F.R.C.S. New York: Dover Publications Inc., 1958 ("authorized and unaltered republication of the work originally published in 1951 . . . by Oxford University Press). Osler was Professor of Medicine at McGill University, the University of Pennsylvania, Johns Hopkins University, and 1905 at Oxford, renowned as a medical historian and considered "the most brilliant and influential teacher of medicine in his day."

PETERSEN, WILLIAM F. (M.D.). *Hippocratic Wisdom for Him Who Wishes to Pursue Properly the Science of Medicine. A Modern Appreciation of Ancient Scientific Achievement.* Springfield, Illinois: Charles C. Thomas Publisher, 1946. The title is a good synopsis of the content and purpose of this work.

POHLENZ, MAX. *Hippokrates und die Begründung der wissenschaftlichen Medizin.* Berlin: Walter de Gruyter, 1938. The foundations of scientific medicine examined.

RIESE, WALTHER and BOURGEY, LOUIS. "Les gracieustés à l'égard des malades. (Commentaire de Galien sur Épidémies, VI, section 4, division 7)," *Revue philosophique de la France et de l'Étranger,* CL 150 (1960), pp. 145–62. Bourgey (see above, under his name) is the translator of the short Galen passage, Riese (see last entry under Galen, above) the interpreter. *Gracieuseté,* from post-classical Latin *gratiositas* is according to Emile Littré a synonym for the French *gratification:* in English we must use words and phrases like kindness, indulgence, respect, courtesy, and benign concern and deference, to convey the same range of meaning as *gracieuseté.* An important though brief contribution to the history of medical education. Riese was subsequently emeritus associate professor of the history of medicine and neurology and psychiatry at the Medical College of

Virginia. "Paying attention to the patient" is a Hippocratic concept of lasting value.

ROSE, HERBERT JENNINGS. *A Handbook of Greek Literature from Homer to the Age of Lucian.* Third edition, revised. London: Methuen & Co., Ltd., 1948. Brief but standard reference work.

SANTILLANA, GIORGIO (DIAZ) DE. *The Origins of Scientific Thought from Anaximander to Proclus,* 600 B.C.–500 A.D. New York: The New American Library, ("A Mentor Book," originally published by The University of Chicago Press), 1961. Ch. 8, "Doctor vs. Medicine Man," pp. 129–40, has a short summary of Hippocratic medicine; most of the chapter is given over to selections from *On the Sacred Disease.* The author was for many years Professor of the History and Philosophy of Science at Massachusetts Institute of Technology.

SARTON, GEORGE. *A History of Science. Ancient Science Through The Golden Age of Greece.* New York: John Wiley & Sons, Inc., 1964 ("Science Editions"). (c1952 by the President and Fellows of Harvard College). A volume dedicated to his Harvard colleague Werner Jaeger and first of eight projected volumes under the same general title by the great Belgian-born historian of science. Chs. XIII, XIV, XV, and XXI are devoted to Greek medicine.

―――. *A History of Science. Hellenistic Science and Culture in the Last Three Centuries B.C.* New York: John Wiley & Sons, Inc. 1965 ("Science Editions"). (c1959 by the President and Fellows of Harvard College.) Vol. 2 of the projected whole work, and the last to receive revision of the typescript (see Foreword, pp. xxi-xxii, by I. Bernard Cohen) by the author. Chs. VIII, IX, and XXII concern Hellenistic (*i.e.,* Greek *and* Roman) medicine. S. died March 22, 1956.

―――. *Introduction to the History of Science. Vol. I: From Homer to Omar Khayyam,* by George Sarton, Associate in the History of Science, Carnegie Institution of Washington. Baltimore: Published for the Carnegie Institution of Washington by The Williams & Wilkins Company, c1927. (*Carnegie Institution of Washington, Publication* No. 376; reprinted 1962.) An invaluable, 839-page *promptuarium* or storehouse serving the initiate as a guide to ancient knowledge of all kinds. Entries for Greek and Roman medicine are numerous: consult introductory chapter, "Contents," and "Index."

SCARBOROUGH, JOHN. *Roman Medicine.* Ithaca, N. Y.: Cornell University Press, 1969. (*Aspects of Greek and Roman Life,* General Editor: H. H. Scullard.) Chs. II and III review Hellenistic medicine, but Hippocratic medicine is not included (but see ch. II, ftn. 1, p. 181). Numerous excellent photographic reproductions including no. 49 (facing p. 137) of the Ostia Museum's Roman copy of a Hellenistic bust of Hippocrates (see under Becatti entry above). S. is Assistant Professor of Ancient History at the University of Kentucky.

SCHOUTEN, JAN. *The Rod and Serpent of Asklepios. Symbol of Medicine.* J. Schouten, Art historian, Director of the Municipal Museums of Gouda, The Netherlands. Amsterdam, London, New York: Elsevier Publishing Company, 1967. A richly illustrated history of the chief insignia of medicine.

SCHUMACHER, JOSEPH. *Die Anfänge abendländischer Medizin in der griechischen Antike.* Stuttgart: W. Kohlhammer Verlag, c1965. S. was named Professor Ordinarius für Geschichte der Medizin in 1964 (director since 1942 of the Medizingeschichtliches Institut of the University of Freiburg in Breisgau. As the title indicates, this essay is primarily a study of the philosophic antecedents of Greek medical development: the 4th, concluding chapter is devoted to the Corpus Hippocraticum.

————. *Antike Medizin. Die naturphilosophischen Grundlagen der Medizin in der griechischen Antike.* Zweite verbesserte Auflage. Berlin: Walter de Gruyter & Co., 1963. ("Diese Ausgabe ist ein im wesentlichen unveränderter Nachdruck des im Jahre 1940 mit der Zusatzbezeichnung "Erster Band" erschienenen Werkes. Das Literaturverzeichnis wurde auf den Stand von 1962 ergänzt.") Dr. Schumacher's paperback book cited above is a condensed version of this earlier work and published as *Urban-Bücher, Die Wissenschaftliche Taschenbuchreihe,* No. 84. The 1963 version has an enlarged bibliography totaling 48 pages.

SHAW, GEORGE BERNARD. *Preface on Doctors. The Doctor's Dilemma.* In *Six Plays by Bernard Shaw, with Prefaces.* New York: Dodd, Mead & Company, 1941, pp. 1-188. Pungent observations in essay and dramatic form on medical practice in the tradition of Molière, Chaucer, Martial, Plautus, and many others besides.

SIGERIST, HENRY E., M.D. *The Great Doctors. A biographical History of Medicine.* Translated by Eden and Cedar Paul. Garden City, N.Y.: Doubleday & Company, Inc. ("Doubleday Anchor Books"), 1958. ("First published in the United States of America 1933 by W. W. Norton & Company, Inc.") (The 1933 English translation was made from the second edition which also appeared that year. S. was director of the Institute of the History of Medicine at Johns Hopkins from 1932 to 1947; he died in 1957, one year after medical history lost George Sarton. Pp. 9-57 cover the seven centuries from Hippocrates to Galen. Like Sarton, Sigerist also projected an eight-volume history of world medicine, of which only two were published (see next entry).

————. *A History of Medicine. Vol. 11: Early Greek, Hindu, and Persian Medicine.* New York: Oxford University Press, 1961. (verso: "Publication No. 38, Department of the History of Medicine, Yale University.) Vol. I (1951) was entitled *Primitive and Archaic Medicine.* The editor of Vol. II was Ludwig Edelstein. Chs. I and IV concern archaic and classic periods of ancient Grek medicine. Numerous illustrations. S. was the pupil and successor of Karl Sudhoff as Director of the Institute of the History of Medicine in the University of Leipzig.

SINGER, CHARLES. *a short history of anatomy from the greeks to harvey.* (The Evolution of Anatomy.) New York: Dover Publications, Inc., c1957. ("unabridged republication of the first edition" [1926?] "with a new Preface by the author, originally published under the title [The Evolution of Anatomy.]"). The words "& Physiology" appear in the title after the word "Anatomy" on the cover of this paperback reprint of the Fitzpatrick Lectures before the College of Physicians. An important complementary work by S. is given below, next.

————. *From Magic to Science. Essays on the Scientific Twilight.* New York: Dover Publications, Inc., c1958. ("unabridged republication of the first edition with an Autobiographical Preface especially written for this edition by the author.") The autobiographical preface referred to on the verso of the title page has a pen portrait of Karl Sudhoff. Both this work and *Short History of Anatomy* are remarkable for the excellence of the illustrations selected. Singer was a pathologist, army medical officer, researcher of herbals, and true founder of medical history in England in this century. It was Sir William Osler who invited S. to Oxford in 1914 in encouragement of his historical interests. Dr. S. is also the author or principal author of, among other works, the important articles in the two reference works referred to in the next two entires.

SINGER, CHARLES and PECK, ARTHUR LESLIE. "Hippocrates and the Hippocratic Collection," *Encyclopaedia Britannica, XI* (1960), pp. 583–85. Summary account of the main facts known.

SINGER, CHARLES. "Medicine," *The Oxford Classical Dictionary,* pp. 548-52. Oxford: At the Clarendon Press, 1949. Thirty-five summary sections on Greek and Roman medical doctrine and practice. Bibliography (selected) arranged in seven sections.

SKINNER, HENRY ALAN. *The Origin of Medical Terms.* Second edition. Baltimore: The William & Wilkins Company, 1961. Etymological notes on approximately 4,000 medical terms. S. is Professor of Anatomy at the University of Western Ontario.

STECKERL, FRITZ. *The Fragments of Praxagoras of Cos and His School.* Collected, edited and translated by Fritz Steckerl. Leiden: E. J. Brill, 1958. (*Philosophia Antiqua, A Series of Monographs on Ancient Philosophy,* edited by W. J. Verdenius and J. H. Waszink, Vol. VIII [132 pp.]). The section "On His Doctrines" (pp. 7–44) gives a general outline the medical system of the fourth century B.C. medical writer. The "School" fragments are from Phylotimus, Plistonicus, and Xenophon. Steckerl is at the Boston University School of Medicine.

Stedman's Medical Dictionary. Twentieth edition, completely revised. Baltimore: The Williams & Wilkins Company, 1961. A standard reference work.

STEUER, ROBERT O. and J. B. DE C. M. SAUNDERS. *Ancient Egyptian and Cnidian Medicine. The Relationship of their Aetiological Concepts of Disease.* Berkeley and Los Angeles: University of California Press, 1959. (verso of t.-p. also lists Cambridge University Press, London, England.) Research based on seven papyri, twelve Hippocratic essays, and essays by Aristotle and Galen. At time of publication of this comparative study of Egyptian *whdw* and Greek *perittoma* ("putrefactive principle"), Steuer was a chemist, Egyptologist, and historian of science. Saunders was Dean of the School of Medicine, University of California, San Francisco.

SUDHOFF, KARL. "Kos und Knidos. Erschautes, erforschtes und durchdachtes aus der südöstlichen Aegaeis, mit 5 Karten und 40 Abbildungen," *Münchener Beiträge zur Geschichte und Literatur der Naturwissenschaften und Medizin,* Heft 4/5, 116 pp., Abb. & Karten (26 plates), herausgegeben von E. Darmstädter. München: MCMXXVII. S. thought the famed plane tree went back only as far as the Turkish occupation of Cos four or five centuries before his visit (pp. 23 f.).

THORWALD, JURGEN. *Histoire de la Médecine dans l'Antiquité.* Texte français de Henry Daussy. (Paris): Hachette, c1962 Droemersche Verlagsansalt, Munich, et Thames and Hudson Limited, Londres. Survey, profusely illustrated, of ancient medicine in Egypt, Mesopotamia, India, China, Mexico, and Peru.

TRACY, THEODORE JAMES, S.J. *Physiological Theory and the Doctrine of the Mean in Plato and Aristotle.* Chicago: Loyola University Press, 1969 (c1969 Mouton & Co. N.V., Publishers, The Hague). Pp. 32–66 are devoted to four Hippocratic works.

VAN BROCK, NADIA. "Recherches sur le vocabulaire médical du grec ancien. Soins et guérison," *Études et Commentaires,* XLI, Paris, Librairie C. Klincksieck, 1961. Philological monograph devoted primarily to four word-families in numerous Greek medical writings of the antique period with the meanings "cure," "heal," "treat," and "healed, healthy, well." Reviewed by John L. Heller in *Language,* Vol. 39, No. 3, Pt. I, July-September, pp. 500–503. The subject was suggested by P. Chantraine. Bibliography pp. xvi-xxiv.

WALTON, ALICE. "The Cult of Asklepios," *Cornell Studies in Classical Philology,* No. III. (no place given): Ginn & Company, 1894 (First reprinting, 1965. Johnson Reprint Corporation.) Review of the then known evidence. See under Edelstein, above.

WELLMAN, MAX. "Hippokrates-Glossare," *Quellen und Studien zur Natur-wissenschaften und der Medizin,* herausgegeben vom Institut für Geschichte der Medizin und der Naturwissenschaften, redigiert von P. Diepgen und J. Ruska, Band 2 (88 pp.). Berlin: Verlag von Julius Springer, 1931. Dr. Wellmann war Ord. Honorar-Professor at the University of Berlin. Glossaries of *termini technici* in the Hippocratic Collection.

WESTERMANN, ANTON. *Biographoi. Vitarum scriptores Graeci minores edidit Antonius Westermann.* Amsterdam: Verlag Adolf M. Hakkert, 1964 ("Nachdruck der Ausgabe Braunschweig, 1845"). The lesser Greek biographers, including those of the medical writers. Texts in Greek.

WOLFLE, DAEL. "The Use of Human Subject," (editorial), *Science,* Vol. 159, No. 3817, 23 February, 1968, p. 831. Commentary on ethical aspect of a recurrent issue in medical practice.

Index